PINACOTECA

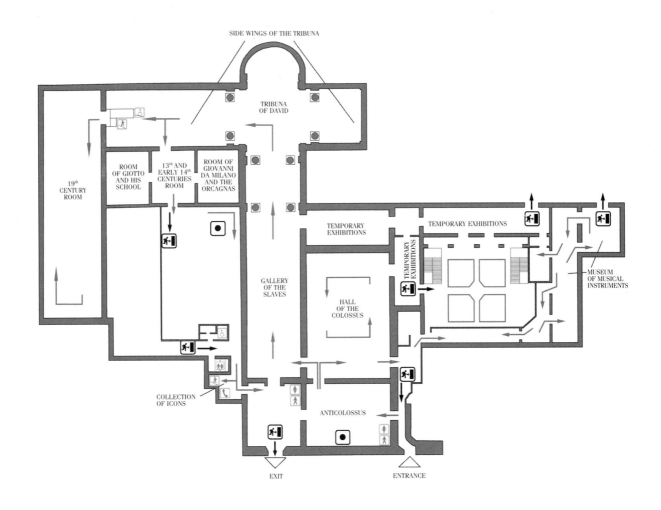

SIDE WINGS OF THE TRIBUNA

TRIBUNA OF DAVID

19th CENTURY ROOM

ROOM OF GIOTTO AND HIS SCHOOL

13th AND EARLY 14th CENTURIES ROOM

ROOM OF GIOVANNI DA MILANO AND THE ORCAGNAS

GALLERY OF THE SLAVES

HALL OF THE COLOSSUS

TEMPORARY EXHIBITIONS

TEMPORARY EXHIBITIONS

TEMPORARY EXHIBITIONS

MUSEUM OF MUSICAL INSTRUMENTS

COLLECTION OF ICONS

ANTICOLOSSUS

EXIT

ENTRANCE

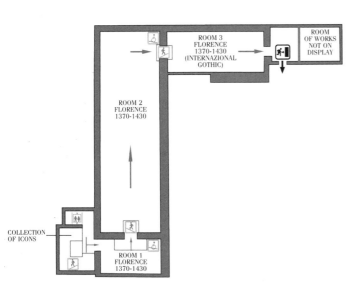

ROOM 3 FLORENCE 1370-1430 (INTERNAZIONAL GOTHIC)

ROOM OF WORKS NOT ON DISPLAY

ROOM 2 FLORENCE 1370-1430

ROOM 1 FLORENCE 1370-1430

COLLECTION OF ICONS

KEY

→ Visitors' itinerary

🚹 🚺 Restrooms

♿ Disabled restrooms

🛗 Lift

🚶 Stairway

♿ Wheelchair access to upper floor

🏃 Emergency exit

📞 Public telephone

⦿ Bookshop

ACCADEMIA GALLERY

The Official Guide
All of the Works

GIUNTI

FIRENZE
MVSEI

Texts
Franca Falletti, Marcella Anglani
Gabriele Rossi Rognoni

Revised by
Francesca Ciaravino *and* Daniela Parenti

Managing Editor
Claudio Pescio

Editor
Augusta Tosone

Translation
Ailsa Wood for Lexis, Florence *and* Catherine Frost

Graphics and page format
Rocío Isabel González *and* Paola Zacchini

Itineraries
Stefano Benini

Photographs
Giunti Archive, Antonio Quattrone *and* Foto Rabatti-Domingie, Florence

This guide is a complete catalogue of all the works exhibited in the Gallery, room by room. The encircled numbers refer to the lists in which all the works are catalogued and indicated with a comment.

www.giunti.it

© 1999, 2011 Ministero dei beni e delle attività culturali e del turismo –
Soprintendenza Speciale per il Patrimonio Storico, Artistico ed Etnoantropologico
e per il Polo Museale della città di Firenze

© 1999, 2011 Giunti Editore S.p.A.
Via Bolognese 165 - 50139 Florence - Italy
Piazza Virgilio 4 - 20123 Milan - Italy

First edition: August 1999
Updated edition: October 2011

"Firenze Mvsei" is a registered trademark
created by Sergio Bianco

Reprint	Year
7 6 5 4 3	2017 2016 2015 2014

Printed by Giunti Industrie Grafiche S.p.A. – Prato (Italy)

Contents

ENOUGH BOOKS HAVE *been written about the public museums in Florence run by the Soprintendenza Speciale per il Patrimonio Storico, Artistico ed Etnoantropologico e per il Polo Museale della città di Firenze to fill a large library. This is hardly surprising when one considers that the artistic heritage preserved in our museums has been famous throughout the world for centuries. For hundreds of years writers, scholars and travellers of every nationality and country have been attempting to describe all that the Florentine museums contain. They have made great efforts to explain why these museums are so fascinating, and to lead a path through paintings and sculptures for both the uninformed but willing visitor and the refined and jaded intellectual.*

Over time, however, the museums have altered their aspect and their layout, the exhibitions have been arranged in new ways, the collections have been enriched (or impoverished). Attributions of works in the museums have also changed, restorations have transformed the appearance of many pieces, the rise and fall of aesthetic tendencies have led to reorganisation and the exhibition of differing works. All these things are constantly taking place within the public collections because museology and the history of art, like any intellectual endeavour, are in a constant state of progress and transformation. This explains why the literature surrounding the Florentine museums (like that of any of the world's great art collections) is so immense, and in a process of continual updating and change.

The perfect, definitive guide to a museum, any museum, does not and cannot exist.

The premise seems obvious, but is nonetheless necessary in order to understand the point of the publication introduced by these lines. From the moment when, in accordance with the application of the Ronchey Law 4/93, the Giunti publishing house group took over the running of the support services within the Florentine museum system, it was decided to start at once on a standardised series of illustrated guides. These guides, displaying the cuneiform flower of "Firenze Musei" on the cover, guarantee that at the year of publication the state of each museum is exactly that described in the guide.

Certain things are obviously necessary if a museum guide is to aspire to reliability, official standing and at the same time enjoy a wide distribution: accuracy of information, high quality reproductions and – not least – a clearly written text (without, naturally, being banal or lacking in precision). Readers will judge for themselves if the guide which follows this introduction reaches these standards. I have no doubt that this will be a serious and committed judgement, just as myself and the Publisher of this guide have been serious and committed in attempting to meet the cultural needs of whoever visits our museums in the best way and with every possible care.

Antonio Paolucci

THE ACCADEMIA GALLERY *possesses and exhibits an amazing display of almost three hundred paintings covering a span of three centuries (Fourteenth, Fifteenth, and Sixteenth), a unique collection of 85 Icons acquired by the Grand Dukes of Lorraine in the mid-Eighteenth century, and a grandiose Nineteenth century gallery of plaster casts including the original models of the major works of Lorenzo Bartolini and Luigi Pampaloni.*

Lastly, in May 2001, a section dedicated to musical instruments was inaugurated, through an agreement stipulated with the nearby 'Luigi Cherubini' State Conservatory of Music, owner of the priceless Collection of instruments that once belonged to the Grand Dukes of Tuscany (the Medici and Lorraine families). The Accademia di Belle Arti from which, as has been seen, this museum originated, had a sector dedicated to musical education, of which the Conservatory is today the heir. With this last acquirement the Galleria has thus re-established links with its historical roots.

A new section now being prepared, that of musical instruments, will open to the public next year, displaying the unique historical collection of the Cherubini Conservatory, linked to the Gallery through special agreements. Obviously, the reasons for visiting this museum are many indeed.

Despite all this, everyone knows that the long, impatient lines of tourists who cross the threshold of the Accademia Gallery each day are really attracted almost exclusively by the myth of Michelangelo's David*. In 1998 there were over a million visitors, many of whom barely glanced at the painting collection and may not even have noticed the Nineteenth century Room. This phenomenon is rather recent, at least in its present frenzied form, and has aroused the curiosity of journalists and authors, historians, psychologists and sociologists. The magic power of the great white fetish is purposely enhanced by the architecture of the hall, which took the shape of a Latin cross when the Gallery of the* Slaves *was built leading up to De Fabris' Tribuna. Moreover, it must be admitted that this hero, already victorious before the fight, represents what modern man is seeking above all else: the reassuring certainty of pure, steadfast strength, a negation of the hesitancy and incertitude of life. And the* Slaves, *with their laborious struggle to emerge from the raw material, seem to have been placed here expressly to arouse an anxiety that the vision of the* David *immediately dispels.*

The heavy sense of the daily struggle to exceed the limitations of human nature is almost overpowering as we enter, but at the back of the great hall lit up by its skylight the world's most famous silhouette already towers above in its stance of classic repose: perfect, calm, in total equilibrium.

Far above any anxious struggle, untouched by defeat, David *exemplifies the secret desire of all.*

History of the Gallery

a

The origins of the Accademia Gallery date back to 1784, when the Grand Duke of Tuscany Pietro Leopoldo brought together various art schools and organizations – such as the Accademia delle Arti del Disegno (Academy of Drawing), founded by Giorgio Vasari under the patronage of Cosimo I in 1563 – to form the new Accademia di Belle Arti (Academy of Fine Arts), a public art school.

Two buildings in particular were restructured to create the new Accademia: the Fourteenth-century Hospital of San Matteo and the Convent of San Niccolò di Cafaggio. The two great hospital wards for men and for women were rebuilt as well-lit galleries designed to stimulate and instruct young people who had chosen art as a career, while providing them with models to copy. Plaster casts, drawings and models were placed in the former mens'

b

a. Moving Michelangelo's *David*
from Piazza della Signoria
to the Accademia
di Belle Arti Gallery,
*from "Nuova Illustrazione
Universale", year I, no. 6,
January 18, 1874, p. 48.*

b. Michelangelo's *David*
during transport
to the Accademia di Belle Arti,
*Photographic Archives
of the Superintendence
for Artistic and Historical
Patrimony of Florence.*

c. Odoardo Borrani,
The Accademia Gallery
in Florence (c. 1860),
*oil on canvas, 25×38 cm,
Galleria Nazionale d'Arte Moderna,
Rome.*

d. Protection placed around
the *David* during World War II.

e. Constructing protection around
the *David*
during World War II.

f. (p. 13) The Tribuna
of *David* in the
Accademia Gallery,
post 1884-ante 1900,
*Alinari Brothers photographic
Archives, photo by Brogi.*

g. (p. 15) The Tribuna of *David*,
post 1911-ante 1930,
*Alinari Brothers photographic
Archives, photo by Brogi.*

ward – adjacent to today's Via Cesare Battisti, on the premises of the Accademia di Belle Arti – while paintings were hung in the former womens' ward, now the Gallery's Nineteenth century Room.

It was for this educational purpose that the first core collection of today's Accademia Gallery was formed.

It included, in addition to two grandiose models by Giambologna – the Rape of the Sabine women and Virtue suppressing Vice – a number of plaster casts of classical statuary and a picture gallery consisting of the original collection of the Accademia del Disegno, which was continuously enriched by paintings transferred here from churches and monasteries suppressed by Pietro Leopoldo in 1786 and then by Napoleon in 1810.

Pietro Leopoldo also decided that works awarded prizes in the newly instituted academ-

ic competitions should be kept on permanent display. This gave rise, over the years, to a gallery presenting a broad sampling of the activity of teachers and pupils, testifying to the variety of artistic trends in Tuscany at the time. The importance of the new acquisitions is recorded in a description by Carlo Colzi in 1817. The Hall of Great Paintings, also known as the Galleria di Mezzogiorno (the present Nineteenth century) contained masterpieces such as the Santa Trinita Virgin by Cimabue, the Adoration of the Magi by Gentile da Fabriano, the Baptism of Christ by Verrocchio and Leonardo, and the Supper at Emmaus by Pontormo, all of which are now in the Uffizi, as well as works still in the Accademia Gallery today, including the decorative tiles from the Santa Croce Reliquary Cabinet by Taddeo Gaddi, the Annunciation by Lorenzo Monaco and the Deposition of Christ by Giovanni da

Milano. *There were also a number of paintings by Beato Angelico, now in the San Marco Museum.*

Not until 1841 was any improvement made in the highly confused arrangement of the paintings, when the President of the Accademia Antonio Ramirez of Montalvo decided to hang them in chronological order to illustrate the history of the Tuscan School from the Fourteenth to the Seventeenth centuries. The remaining Thirteenth and Fourteenth century paintings of unknown attribution or in poor state of conservation were left in the Antique Paintings Gallery (now the Hall of the Slaves) where they were so numerous as to entirely cover the walls. In 1817 there was also a "Prize-winning Works Room" containing eighteen works of art awarded first prize in the triennial painting and sculpture competitions. In 1821 this modern section was enlarged by the addition of prize-winning works from the annual Emulation and Pensionato competitions, all of which remained the property of the Accademia.

When Florence became capital of Italy at the time of the Unification, the city's museums, including the Accademia, underwent great changes. A new addition was the Modern Gallery, consisting of onehundredfortysix works transferred from Palazzo della Crocetta and arranged in six small rooms on the first floor of the Accademia that had previously belonged to the School of Declamation.

The Gallery thus became the first museum of modern art in the new State of Italy. From then on it was mentioned in all of the guidebooks as the Antique and Modern Gallery and increasingly recognized as an attraction for curious travellers as well a place for young artists to study innovations in Florentine art. Numerous requests were made to copy the paintings, the modern ones in particular, clearly demonstrating that the various collections still found a common denominator in the Gallery's educational mission.

In 1872 the museum structure was revolutionized when the Municipal Government decided to build a new room at the end of the Antique Paintings Gallery to house Michelangelo's David, which urgently needed to be moved from its unsheltered outdoor loca-

tion in Piazza della Signoria. *The architect assigned this task, Emilio De Fabris, designed an impressive Tribune which, placed scenographically at the end of the Antique Paintings Gallery and lighted from above by a skylight in the roof, was to welcome the David as the greatest of masterpieces. In early August 1873 the David, sliding on rails through the city streets, was transported to the Accademia where it was left enclosed in a wooden scaffolding for nine years while the Tribuna was being finished.*

The arrival of the David and the project for building the Tribuna were crucial events for the fate of the Gallery. In 1875, on the occasion of the fourth centenary of Michelangelo's birth, the Accademia was deemed the most appropriate place to hold an exhibition of copies of the great artist's works. Exhibiting the plaster casts here would have found a valid rationale in the presence of the David, the reference point for the show, in a relationship of mutual enhancement. To create a space large enough for the exhibition it was requested that changes be made in the design of the Tribuna. No longer a square hall, it was to be shaped like a Greek cross. The right wing of the cross would then be extended to connect the Antique Paintings Gallery, then known as the Beato Angelico Gallery, to the parallel one of the Great Paintings, or of Perugino. The Michelangelo exhibition was by far the most important event in the centenary festivities held in Florence on September 13-16, 1875. For the occasion the Tribuna was draped with curtains to conceal the still-unfinished arches and vaults above the trabeation.

The wooden scaffolding was removed and the David, the only original statue in the show, became the fulcrum point of the entire exhibition, towering over all. This event had important museological consequences, giving decisive impetus to the creation of a Michelangelo Museum containing the plaster casts and photographs donated to the City of Florence. With farsighted intuition De Fabris wrote in 1877: 'Should the Tribuna be completed, and the Michelangelo Museum inaugurated, it is certain that the proceeds from the sale of tickets would increase substantially, considering that while the importance of the gallery

now is only relative, it would then become so great that no foreigner would come to Florence without visiting it'.

The architect Emilio De Fabris was the true artificer of the Michelangelo Museum, inaugurated on July 22, 1882. In the vestibule of the Tribuna, plaster casts of the Medici Tombs were placed against the walls with the seated statues of Lorenzo and Giuliano de' Medici above them. At the back of the Tribuna's left wing, the shorter one, stood the Moses. In the right wing were plaster casts of the artist's most famous works; at the center, under the tribunal arch, was a copy of the St. Peter's Pietà, while copies of the Rondanini Pietà and the Minerva Christ were placed at the corners of the piers.

In that same 1882 management of the Accademia's Antique and Modern Gallery was transferred from the Fine Arts Institute to the Museums Bureau, causing the conservational, historical and documentary functions of the museum to prevail over the promotional program for contemporary art. In fact, as long as academic teaching methods had been based on the exercise of copying, the picture gallery had remained closely bound to the Accademia's painting School. When that method was abandoned as obsolete and inconsonant with the needs of contemporary art, the emancipation of the galleries from academic control became an urgent necessity.

The separation of the Antique and Modern Gallery from the art school was underlined by the opening of a new entrance in Via Ricasoli and by re-arrangement of the Michelangelo Museum.

The position of the Tribuna remained the same up to the early Twentieth century, while the Antique Paintings sector underwent major changes that marked the end of a trend of scientific and vaguely positivistic museum culture. Moreover, the concept of the museum as a structure dedicated exclusively to conservation was undergoing revision at this time, in relation to a new way of confronting works of art, now considered to be the subject of pure contemplation and 'not a series of objects to be arranged in rows like insects by entomologists, but living things'.

These new museum concepts was to influ-

ence the program for rearranging the Florentine galleries carried out by Cosimo Ridolfi, the Director from 1890 to 1903.

During this period the Accademia Gallery definitively lost its original characteristics, as profound changes were made. In the first place, the works of art in the Great Paintings Gallery urgently needed restoration, and this was favorable to a new arrangement. Wooden partitions were used to divide the room into three areas, separating the Fourteenth and Fifteenth century paintings from those of the Seventeenth century.

Three new rooms were also created (the former Byzantine Rooms the actually Thirteenth and Early Fourteenth centuries Room, Room of Giovanni da Milano and the Orcagnas, Room of Giotto and his School) along the left wing of the Tribuna, providing a more dignified and luminous setting for the paintings of Botticelli (to whom two of the rooms were dedicated), of Perugino and their pupils. Ridolfi made these changes to adapt the Accademia Gallery to the new aesthetic appreciation of the Florentine Fifteenth Century School then being proclaimed mainly by British collectors living in Florence.

The rediscovery of Botticelli, which had begun with Pater's studies and been confirmed by the extensive monograph written by Herbert Horne during his years in Florence, was becoming a real cult in the early years of the Twentieth century, generating great public enthusiasm. A period of renewed popularity suddenly opened up for the Accademia Gallery, with its numerous Fifteenth century paintings. With the dignity and prominence conferred on them by their new arrangement, these paintings became a pole of attraction equal to or greater than that of the David and Michelangelo's other works.

Ridolfi then decided to put in "more appropriate state" the hall leading to the Tribuna, where Thirteenth and Fourteenth century panels and polyptychs were amassed in utter confusion. Radical changes were made in the arrangement of this hall. The paintings were removed and the walls adorned with rich tapestries depicting Stories of Adam and Eve. Plaster casts of some of Michelangelo's minor works were placed along both side walls. The

paintings that had been removed were then hung in the three rooms adjoining the Hall (formerly the Florentine Rooms), suitably decorated and lighted, the first of which was dedicated to Beato Angelico. This arrangement lasted only a few years since in 1919 works of capital importance to the Florentine School – Giotto and Cimabue's Majesty, Gentile da Fabriano's Adoration of the Magi, Masolino and Masaccio's Saint Anne Metterza, Botticelli's Primavera and many others – were moved to the Uffizi Gallery, and in 1922 the conspicuous group of paintings by Beato Angelico went to establish the new San Marco Museum. Almost contemporaneously, in 1914, an agreement was stipulated between the State and the Municipality to group various collections of modern art in a single museum set up in 1920 on the second floor of Palazzo Pitti. The modern works of the Accademia Gallery, in part dispersed among various State and Municipal storage deposits, were transferred to their new home.

After having lost so many of its paintings the Gallery could no longer call itself the Antique and Modern Gallery. From now on it was to be Accademia Gallery or, for a few more years, Michelangelo Museum. The arrangement of the latter has also undergone numerous changes up to the present.

Controversy over the arrangement of the museum flared up again in the first decade of the Twentieth century, in relation to the question of placing a copy of the David in Piazza della Signoria. The presence of plaster casts in a public gallery, inserted within a context still linked to educational ideals and positivist/historical objectives, now seemed entirely unjustified. In line with the new aesthetic canons, authenticity became the guiding principle of the Gallery's Director Corrado Ricci, and most of the plaster casts kept here since the centenary exhibition were removed and replaced by original works of Michelangelo. At the same time, national newspapers were calling attention to the poor state of the Slaves in Buontalenti's Grotto in the Boboli Gardens, and to the St. Matthew 'drowsing under the atrium of the Accademia'. The Slaves were removed from Boboli, replaced by copies, and transferred to the Accademia Gallery in 1909.

That same year the School of Accademia delle Belle Arti, which had already contributed the model of the Fiume Torso in 1906, donated the St. Matthew. This group of works was further enriched by the Victory, transferred from the Bargello Museum in 1905. The plaster casts from the centenary exhibition, arranged by Ridolfi along the walls hung with tapestries, were replaced by the originals of the Slaves, the St. Matthew and the Victory, along with two plaster casts of the Louvre Slaves, while the model of the Fiume Torso was placed under the right arch of the Tribuna. The plaster casts of the Tombs, the Moses, the Rondanini Pietà, the Minerva Christ and the Vatican Pietà remained in their original places. In Ricci's arrangement based on the principle of authenticity, even these last plaster casts soon appeared inappropriate. However, it was only in 1938 that the casts of the two Pietà, the Moses, the Minerva Christ and the Tombs were definitively moved to the Plaster Casts Collection of the Porta Romana Art School. The two casts of the Slaves were the last to leave the Accademia in 1946, transferred first to the Casa Buonarroti Museum, then to the House of Michelangelo in Caprese, where a conspicuous group of casts from the centennial exhibition can still be seen today.

The collection of the originals also underwent changes before taking on its present-day aspect. In 1921, with the closure of the Dante Year and the celebration of victory in World War I, Ugo Ojetti suggested that, for the occasion, the Victory should be brought back to the Hall of the Five Hundred in Palazzo Vecchio. In 1939 the State of Italy purchased for the Accademia the Palestrina Pietà, coming from a chapel in Palazzo Barberini at Palestrina, the authenticity of which is now denied by the most authoritative scholars. Lastly, in 1965, the Fiume Torso was requested by Charles Tolnay, to join the other models in the Casa Buonarroti.

In the 1930s the Hall of the Colossus and that of the Anticolossus were annexed to the Gallery. These large rooms provided a perfect setting for the great altarpieces of the Florentine Sixteenth century masters such as Massimo Albertinelli, Bronzino, Alessandro Allori, Santi di Tito and Passignano.

After the war, during rearrangement of the Uffizi Gallery, some large paintings were moved to the Accademia, including the Sixteenth century Assumption by Perugino and Deposition by Perugino and Filippino Lippi.

In the 1950s, under the direction of Luisa Becherucci, the Hall of the Colossus, illustrating the course of art in the Fifteenth and Sixteenth centuries, was organized on a more historical basis, as can be seen in the works of Perugino, Fra Bartolomeo, Granacci, Bugiardini and Sogliani. In the Hall of the Anticolossus, now occupied by the bookshop and ticket office, were placed some works coming from the Uffizi, including the Young St. John from the school of Raphael and the Venus and Cupid by Pontormo. These works, in addition to those of Bronzino and Allori already present, clearly illustrated the development of the "modern manner" in the Sixteenth century. Only in the 1980s was this arrangement dismantled and the paintings hung in the Tribuna in place of the tapestries, to underline their direct and indirect relationship with the work of Michelangelo.

Subsequent Directors have opposed the tendency – which had emerged in the post-World War I period – to proceed without a specific direction or long-term project. From direction of Luciano Bellosi, through the important years of Giorgio Bonsanti, up to the current Director Franca Falletti, a continuous attempt has been made to trace a guiding principle on which to construct the identity of the Accademia Gallery.

This project took concrete shape in the years between 1983 and 1985 with the arrangement of the Nineteenth century Room and that of the Late Fourteenth century Room on the first floor, supervised by Angelo Tartuferi in 1998 and renovated in 2011 by Daniela Parenti. The opening to the public of the latter rooms confirmed the museum's chronological, stylistic and historical direction, providing a continuous panorama, albeit in different groups of rooms, of Florentine art from the late Thirteenth to the late Sixteenth centuries, in accordance with the original principles of the Accademia as conceived by Pietro Leopoldo. What now re-emerges in all its significance is the value of the Accademia as school of instruction and exemplification of the highest artistic manifestations in three centuries of history. Within this context, the Collection of Russian Icons on the first floor also testifies to the precious heritage of the Lorraine family.

The Nineteenth century Room, with the plaster casts by Bartolini and Pampaloni and the paintings, few but significant, by pupils and professors of the Accademia di Belle Arti, unites the Accademia to the Gallery, rebuilding a bridge of historical significance and recalling how Accademia and Gallery were once joined in a common project to produce and nourish art.

As the origins of the Gallery have been retrieved, links with the adjoining Cherubini Conservatory and Opificio delle Pietre Dure have inevitably been restored. All of these institutions, in fact, grew out of a unified project, perhaps the most culturally significant initiative of the Lorraine government, that of constructing, in the block between today's Via Ricasoli, Via degli Alfani, Via dei Servi and Via Cesare Battisti, a true citadel of the arts. This is the basis for the current Director's project, in which a Museum of Musical Instruments, containing the historic collection of the Cherubini Conservatory, has been opened to the public. And it is possible that in the near future the itinerary may be completed by coordinated access to the Museum of the Opificio delle Pietre Dure, next door to the Cherubini Conservatory.

Marcella Anglani

The Museum of Musical Instruments

The Museum of Musical Instruments in the Accademia Gallery, inaugurated in 2001, currently exhibits over forty instruments from the 17th, 18th and 19th centuries, coming from the Grand-Ducal collections of the Medici and Lorraine families. The collection is owned by the "Luigi Cherubini" Conservatory of Florence, which received the instruments and carefully preserved them since the 19th century. The exhibition includes some objects unique the world over, such as the Tenor Viola by Antonio Stradivari, the only instrument created by the famous violin-maker which has been entirely kept in its original state; the earliest known example of an Upright Piano; and an Oval Spinet, the first instrument constructed for the Medici family by the inventor of the piano, Bartolomeo Cristofori. The cultural and musical context for which these instruments were created is illustrated by some seventeenth-century paintings portraying musicians and their instruments at the Medicean Court. In addition, a computerized multimedia system provides visitors with information in Italian and English on the history and particular features of these instruments, and even allows them to hear their sound. In addition, some models which can be actuated by visitors illustrate the action of the first Piano, invented at the Medicean Court in the late 17th century, and show how this instrument differs from its forerunner, the Harpsichord. A room dedicated to Alessandro Kraus, a Florentine collector from the late 19th century who owned over a thousand instruments coming from all over the world, has recently been added to the Museum. Some of these instruments recently donated to the Museum by a descendent of the collector, Mirella Gatti-Kraus, are displayed here.

Anton Domenico Gabbiani
The Grand Prince Ferdinando with his Musicians

Music played a primary role in the official celebrations of the Medicean Court, as another manifestation of the dynasty's power. A vivacious musical current independent of State occasions was promoted in particular by the son of Cosimo III, Grand Prince Ferdinando, himself a musician

and lover of music who attracted to Florence such composers as Haendel and Scarlatti. His interest in music also led him to build up an extraordinary collection of over one hundred musical instruments, some of them from the hands of the most famous makers of the epoch. The instruments displayed in the first section of the Museum come from his collection. The musicians and their instruments at the Court of Ferdinando were portrayed by Anton Domenico Gabbiani in a cycle of canvases painted between 1685 and 1690. These representations are so faithful that it has been possible in some cases to identify the personages and to recognize the instruments from the descriptions in the Medicean Inventories.

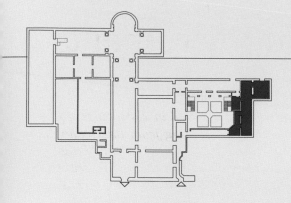

2 4

THE MEDICEAN VIOLONCELLOS

The three Cellos are listed in an Inventory of the instruments belonging to the personal collection of Grand Prince Ferdinando de' Medici, compiled in the year 1700. The one bearing the Medici coat-of-arms was built by the violin-maker from Cremona Nicolò Amati, active between 1630 and 1670, and probably the master of Antonio Stradivari. The body of the instrument, originally larger, was 'trimmed' in the late 18th century to reduce its size to the dimensions that had become standard for cellos after the beginning of 1700.

NICOLÒ AMATI
Violoncello

Cremona, c. 1650
Red spruce and maple wood

Total length 122 cm
Body measurements:
length 75,7 cm;
maximum width 45,7 cm
Inv. Cherubini 1988/33

5

MARBLE SALTERIO

The dulcimer is an instrument that was extraordinarily popular in Italy in the 17th and 18th centuries, only to disappear completely in the Romantic age. With the ingenious arrangement of the strings, which were plucked with plectra fastened to the fingertips, a wide range of notes can be played with this small instrument. The one exhibited here is truly unique in that it is entirely constructed of marble of three different kinds (white statuary marble, bardiglio from Carrara and yellow broccatello) rather than wood. The dedication and the painting on the cover of the case show that it was built for Grand Duke Cosimo III de' Medici, the father of Grand Prince Ferdinando, after 1691. It was probably the work of the same artisan who built for the Este family a *Guitar*, a *Violin*, a *Harpsichord* and various wind instruments, all in the same material. Although these instruments were designed primarily as decorative objects, they could perfectly well be played.

MICHELE ANTONIO GRANDI
(ATTR.)
Marble Salterio
Carrare (?), After 1691

Statuary marble, bardiglio, and yellow broccatello
Maximum width 74,5 cm;
depth 30 cm
Inv. Cherubini 1988/88

6–7 THE MEDICEAN QUINTET

The *Tenor Viola* and the *Violoncello* formed part of a "quintet" of string instruments (two *Violins*, an *Alto Viola*, a *Tenor Viola* and a *Violoncello*) built by the master from Cremona Antonio Stradivari for Grand Prince Ferdinando and dated 1690. The five instruments were all decorated with the Medici coat-of-arms in mother-of-pearl, and with ebony and ivory inlays. The chosen woods, of exceptional quality, combined excellent sound with the highest aesthetic value. The *Tenor Viola* is the only instrument in the world made by Antonio Stradivari to be entirely conserved in its original state; as such, it represents a document of inestimable importance for violin-makers and music scholars. The large size of the *Viola* body, like that of the *Violoncello*, intensifies the bass sounds and confers on the instruments a characteristic deep timbre.

ANTONIO STRADIVARI
"Medici" Tenor Viola
Cremona, 1690
Red spruce and maple wood

Total length 75,5 cm
Body measurements:
length 47,8 cm;
maximum width 27,1 cm
Inv. Cherubini 1988/15

10–12 VIOLINS

The three *Violins* were acquired for the Grand-Ducal Collection at a relatively late time (after 1814), but were constructed during the lifetime of Grand Prince Ferdinando. The red-varnished *Violin* is one of the best conserved instruments built by Antonio Stradivari. It dates from the period of full stylistic maturity of the Master, who established the classic proportions and lines for the violin makers in Cremona, still today taken as model by violin-makers all over the world. The other two instruments, of the Modena and the Po Valley schools, differ from each other in the color of the varnish, the contour of the belly, the shape of the f-holes and the form of the scroll. On the basis of this and other stylistic features, their authorship (falsely indicated on labels glued to the inside of the body) has been questioned and the current attribution has been proposed.

ANTONIO STRADIVARI
"Medici" Violin

Cremona, 1716
Red spruce
and maple wood
Total length 59,7 cm
Body measurements:
length 35,8 cm;
maximum width 20,8 cm
Inv. Cherubini 1988/3

KEYBOARD INSTRUMENTS

The *Piano*, a keyboard instrument whose strings are struck by hammers, was invented in Florence shortly before 1700 by a Paduan instrument-maker, Bartolomeo Cristofori, at the service of Grand Prince Ferdinando, and was only the most long-lasting of his numerous and ingenious inventions. Exhibited in the same room is the first instrument created by him for the Medici: a *Spinet* recently rediscovered, whose form, action and sonority were entirely designed by Cristofori. Dating from slightly later, also built for the Medici, is a *Harpsichord* constructed entirely of ebony wood. The action displayed at the left of the *Spinet* seems instead to come from a pianoforte dating from Cristofori's time, although its attribution to a specific maker is still debatable. The instrument displayed on the opposite side of the hall is the earliest known *Upright Piano*. It was built in 1739, seven years after the death of Cristofori, by an instrument-maker who may have been his assistant, Domenico del Mela.

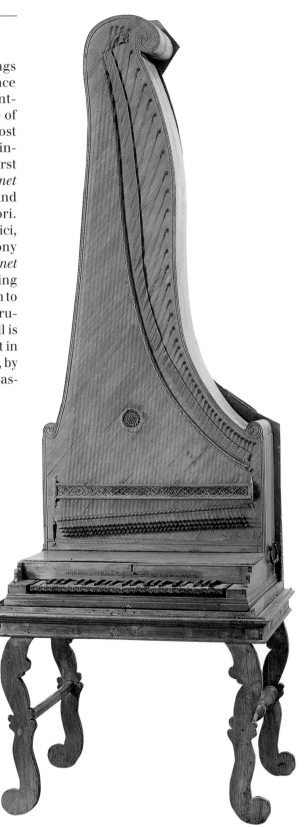

DOMENICO DEL MELA
Upright Piano

Galliano nel Mugello (Florence), 1739

Coniferous wood, cypress and boxwood
Total height 273 cm; width 93 cm; depth 64 cm
Compass: Do1/Mi1-Do5 (C/E-c''')
Inv. Cherubini 1988/110

MUSIC IN THE LORRAINE AGE

When the sovereignty of the Grand-Duchy of Tuscany passed from the Medici family (which died out in 1737) to the Austrian one of the Lorraines, radical changes occurred in the musical life of the Court and that of the entire city. Grand Duke Pietro Leopoldo (ruler of Florence from 1765) promoted public musical events, held in the streets and squares, as well as celebrations open on occasion to the citizens as a whole. This new approach was reflected in the collection of musical instruments as well. Many of the instruments from Medicean times, worn and unsuited to the new activity of the Court, were sold or discarded, and new ones – wind and percussion instruments in particular – were purchased and imported from abroad.

PERCUSSION INSTRUMENTS

The percussion instruments exhibited here represent one of the very rare homogenous groups of this kind which has survived from the late 18th century. These instruments were used for the most part in theatrical performances and Court balls. Among them is the oldest pair of *Kettledrums* in Italy, equipped with a tuning mechanism, in addition to pairs of *Jingles* used 'for the waltz of the whip', *Xylophones*, *Castanets* and *Triangles*.

JOHANN CASPAR JOSEPH EINBIGLER (?)
Pair of kettle-drums
c. 1857

Copper, iron, leather
Height of the drumhead
from the ground 80 cm;
diameter of the drumheads:
50/53 cm
Inv. Cherubini 1988/199, 209

23

WIND INSTRUMENTS

After the Restoration of the Lorraines in 1814, subsequent to fifteen years of French domination, various wind instruments were purchased for both theatrical use and performances of the Grand-Ducal band. The brass instruments, *Horns* and *Trombones*, were imported from Germany and Austria and may have been brought to Florence by members of the Court. The provenance of the little *Post-horn* (before 1819) is instead unknown, but the instrument is of a type that had been commonly used since the early 16th century by couriers in the postal service to announce their arrival at a post station. In the nineteenth century the little instrument was used to limited extent for special effects in the orchestra. The next display case holds wind instruments made of wood. Some of them, a *Piccolo* (before 1806), a *Basset-Horn* (1810-1819) and the five *Clarinets* (from about 1838) are furnished with *corps de rechange* which could be substituted to the original ones to change the intonation and make it more acute. Some others, such as the *Serpent* and the above-mentioned *Basset-Horn*, are constructed so that the size of these quite long instruments can be reduced, making them more manageable. The *Serpent* was widely used as bass accompaniment for religious and military music, while passages for the *Basset-Horn* were composed by W. A. Mozart, among others.

LORENZO CERINO
Serpent
Turin, late 18th century

Chestnut wood (?)
and leather
Overall length 86 cm;
length of tube about 195 cm
Inv. Cherubini 1988/175

THE TRUMPET MARINE

The sound of this instrument with a single catgut string is extraordinarily similar to that of a trumpet, thanks to an asymmetrical bridge that rests on only one of its two feet, while the other rattles on the soundboard when the string is bowed. This instrument, which entered the Grand-Ducal Collection in the late 18th century, was used in musical performances held at the Lorraine Court until the 1830s.

It was specifically required in the score of an opera presented at Court, the *Socrate immaginario* by Giovanni Paisiello, in which an instrumental solo is followed by an aria ('Questa corda non s'accorda al dio Amor' [this string is not in tune with the god of Love]), a humorous allusion to the instrument's harsh timbre.

ANONYMOUS
Trumpet Marine

Late 18th century

White spruce, cherry
and walnut wood
Total height 162,4 cm;
maximum width 29,2 cm
Inv. Cherubini 1988/47

HURDY-GURDIES

The sound of the *Hurdy-gurdy* is produced by a number of strings set in vibration by a wooden wheel coated with rosin, driven by a crank, which strokes the strings like the bow of a violin. The notes are produced by pressing a series of keys on the side with the left hand. Instruments based on this principle had been known in Europe since the 13th century, but only in the 18th this model, richly decorated with mother-of-pearl and inlays, was developed specifically for amateur musicians among the nobility. The *Hurdy-gurdy* became especially popular in France, since the wife of Louis XV was in fact an accomplished player on this instrument. In a parallel development, a "popular" model, much cruder in appearance but functioning in the same way and used mainly by beggars, survived throughout the 19th century.

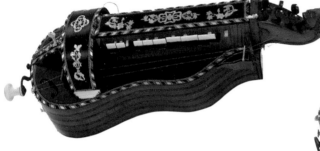

JEAN NICOLAS LAMBERT
Pair of Hurdy-gurdies

Paris, 1775

Mahogany, maple, beech, ebony, ivory
Body measurements:
length 46,1 cm;
maximum width 24,5 cm
Inv. Cherubini 1988/50-51

THE VIOLA AND THE GUITARS

The *Viola*, the *Piano-Guitar* and the *Guitar with six strings* entered the Lorraine Collection in the early 19th century. The *Viola* (1774) presents the typical characteristics of a German-made instrument: dark varnish, short, vertical f-holes, pronounced arching of the belly and back. The *Piano-Guitar* is, instead, an instrument constructed in the United States near the end of the 18th century, but designed in Great Britain as a particular version of the *English Guitar*, with drop-shape case, flat belly and back. It was an instrument designed for well-brought up young girls, in which the strings are struck by a series of hammers actioned by six keys, ensuring that the player's fingertips are not roughened. The *Guitar with six strings*, despite some modifications made to the original structure, has kept the slender proportions of the body typical of instruments built in the first half of the 19th century. This instrument was played, it seems, by Queen Maria Luisa di Borbone-Parma (1807).

ANONYMOUS
Guitar with six strings

ante 1804
Spruce and exotic wood
Total length 91,5 cm
Body measurements:
length 43,2 cm
maximum width 26,1 cm
Inv. Cherubini 1988/73

Hall of the Colossus

The name of this room is not, as is usually believed, taken from Giambologna's plaster model, now placed at its center, but from the model of one of the Dioscuri *of Montecavallo, displayed here in the 19th century. The panels exhibited here belong to 15th and early 16th century Forentine painting. They include masterpieces such as the canvas depicting* Scenes of Monastic Life *by Paolo Uccello and the* Madonna and Child with the Young Saint John and Two Angels *by Botticelli. The production of the most important workshops of Renaissance Florence, such as those of Ghirlandaio, Cosimo Rosselli, Perugino and Filippino Lippi, is also represented; there, in fact, the great masters worked in close contact with assistants and apprentices to produce the numerous paintings destined to adorn the thousand altars of the city's churches, both large and small.*

①

GIAMBOLOGNA
Rape of the Sabine Women

This is the plaster model for the marble sculptured group which can be seen under Loggia dei Lanzi in Piazza della Signoria. Giambologna's virtuosity here ventures to create for the first time a large-sized marble sculpture with a tightly-knit group of three figures, which almost form a single body, in a circular spiral movement seemingly without beginning or end. When the group was sculpted (1582) it did not have a definite subject but was presented by the artist as a simple exercise in skill; only later was it given the title *Rape of the Sabine Women*.

3

PAOLO UCCELLO
Scenes of Hermit life
(or *Thebaid*)

The subject of this painting by Paolo Uccello is not easily interpreted but is certainly linked to a path of meditation and spiritual improvement through prayer. The following episodes can be identified: *The stigmata of St. Francis*, *St. Jerome worships the Crucifix*, *The appearance of the Virgin to St. Bernard* and *St. Benedict preaches to his brethren*.

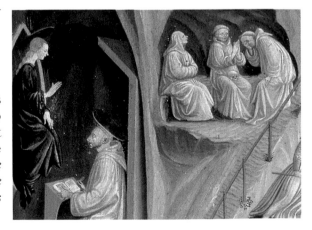

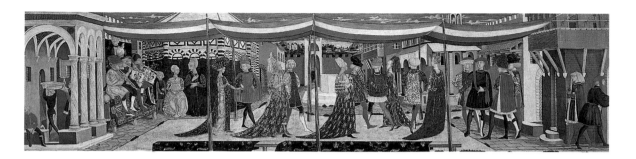

9

LO SCHEGGIA
Wedding procession
or *Cassone (Chest) Adimari*

This was originally listed as *Cassone Adimari* because it was thought to be the front panel of a wedding chest belonging to the Adimari family. The painting (c. 1450) was later recognised as part of a "spalliera", a wall decoration, and was attributed to Giovanni di Ser Giovanni, known as Lo Scheggia, the brother of Masaccio. The images depicted here concern a wedding feast and portray the streets, monuments (the Baptistry can be seen on the left), landscapes and customs of Renaissance Florence with vivacity and extraordinary wealth of detail.

10

SANDRO BOTTICELLI
Madonna and Child
with the infant St. John and two Angels

This work, from Botticelli's early phase, the
clearly shows the stylistic characteristics of Fi-
lippo Lippi, in whose studio Sandro Botticelli
was still training. This composition with its
diffuse structure was to be very successful in
later years and was repeated in numerous ter-
racotta bas-reliefs for private devotional use.

16

SANDRO BOTTICELLI (?)
Madonna of the Sea

This small panel (c. 1475-1480), which owes its name to the dim seascape in the background, has always been one of the most admired works by visitors to the Gallery.
However the critics are still not in agreement over the attribution, vacillating between Botticelli and Filippino Lippi.

NERI DI BICCI
Annunciation

This panel comes from the Church of Santa Maria del Sepolcro, known as "delle Campora", for which it was commissioned in 1464 by Agnolo Vettori, an outstanding figure in Fifteenth century Florentine politics, several times prior and gonfalonier of the Republic in 1458.

Heir to an ancient Florentine studio, founded by his grandfather Lorenzo di Bicci and continued by his father, Bicci di Lorenzo, Neri di Bicci often reproduced traditional compositions over the years with his impeccable technique, making only the slightest modifications.

Worthy of note in this *Annunciation* is the detail of the small board at the bottom showing the *Crucifixion*, and the complex architecture where the deep perspective leads the gaze to the landscape in the background.

COSIMO ROSSELLI
St. Barbara between
St. John the Baptist and St. Matthew

Cosimo Rosselli, head of a well-equipped, active family-run studio, painted this gorgeous panel for the Chapel of St. Barbara and St. Quiricus in the Basilica of Santissima Annunziata in Florence. This chapel belonged to the so-called "Teutonic Nation", i.e. to the Germans and Flemings.

St. Barbara was the patron saint of artillery and therefore she is holding up the tower as a symbol of a line of fortification and crushing a conquered warrior beneath her feet. The composition of the painting (c. 1470) recalls details from works by other contemporary Florentine artists, like Pollaiuolo's panel for the Portuguese cardinal's Chapel in San Miniato and Ghirlandaio's fresco in the Church of Sant'Andrea in Cercina, and it is painted with skill and dignity.

36

ANDREA DI GIUSTO
Virgin of the Girdle and Saints

This painting, dated 1437 and signed "Andrea de Florentia", comes from the Church of Santa Margherita in Cortona, and is the work of a painter active during the first half of the 15th century.

The artist is clearly familiar with the great "modern" painters, such as Paolo Uccello and Beato Angelico, but solidly linked to the Gothic tradition, as this altarpiece shows in its use of gold-leaf background and the division of the space into three.

This work is especially interesting for its completeness, having come down to us intact in all its parts: the crown, the slender lateral pillars, the predella and the bases of the pillars with the two kneeling donors.

40

GIOVANNI ANTONIO SOGLIANI
*Dispute concerning
the Immaculate Conception*

This panel shows the Doctors of the Church gathered around the body of Adam discussing the question of the Immaculate Conception of the Virgin, a theme also depicted in Carlo Portelli's panel. This work belongs to the specific historical period in which the Catholic Church was particularly intent on consolidating the Marian cult against diffusion of the Lutheran heresy.

35

46

LORENZO DI CREDI
Adoration of the Child

The original location of this painting by Lorenzo di Credi is uncertain, some experts believing it to come from the Convento dell'Annun- ziata, others from the Convento delle Murate. Painted slightly later than the better known *Adoration* in the Uffizi Gallery (c. 1480-1485), it dates to the last decade in the Fifteenth century, a period in which Renaissance style was undergoing dissolution.

Lorenzo di Credi assimilated Leonardo's innovations (both were pupils of Verrocchio) up to the point where they represented a break with the past. In this painting the symmetrical scheme, the view scaled plane by plane, and the sentimental effects of the figures testify to Lorenzo's rejection of Leonardo's perspective studies as well as his links to Fifteenth century tradition. In the landscape in the background and the small figures of shepherds at the left, the quality of the painting is reminiscent of Piero di Cosimo.

52-49

FRA BARTOLOMEO

The Prophet Isaiah (on the left)
The Prophet Job (on the right)

These two recently restored panels came from the Billi Chapel in the Basilica of Santissima Annunziata in Florence. At their centre was the *Salvator Mundi and the four Evangelists*, today on show in the Palatina Gallery. Cardinal Carlo

de' Medici purchased the three panels in 1631 and placed them in the Medici house in Piazza San Marco. In 1697 Prince Ferdinand took the central altarpiece to Palazzo Pitti as part of his personal collection, while the two Prophets were passed on to the Uffizi and then to the Accademia. The two Prophets were painted by Fra Bartolomeo immediately after his journey to Rome (c. 1514-1516), and are evidence of his meditations on Michelangelo's Sistine Chapel.

50

FILIPPINO LIPPI AND PIETRO PERUGINO
Deposition

This painting was part of a grand wooden group commissioned by the friars of Santissima Annunziata of Florence. Filippino Lippi began work on it in 1504 and finished the upper part except for the body of Christ; he then died, and the work was completed in 1507 by Perugino who also painted the other panels to be inserted in the complex structure.

FILIPPINO LIPPI
St. John the Baptist
St. Mary Magdalene

These two paintings (c. 1496) were the side panels of an altarpiece having at the center a *Crucifixion with the Virgin and St. Francis* with gold-leaf background, originally placed in the Chapel of Francesco Valori in San Procolo.

The panels were divided in the mid-Eighteenth century and the central one was destroyed in Berlin in 1945 during World War II.

The two figures in the side panels, St. John the Baptist, consumed by repentance in the desert, and St. Mary Magdalene, are marked by the suffering of spiritual torment, emphasized by their emaciated appearance, tangled hair, torn clothing and bare feet.

In these figures Filippino revived the figurative tradition of the early Fifteenth century, especially as exemplified in polychrome wooden sculptures, to suggest the devout objective of art according to the dictates of the client Valori, one of Girolamo Savonarola's most important followers.

51

DOMENICO GHIRLANDAIO
St. Stephen between
St. James and St. Peter

In the past this panel was attributed to Sebastiano Mainardi, a pupil of Ghirlandaio, but it was recently recognised as work of the master himself. A few years after it was painted, perhaps in 1513, the figure of St. Stephen was repainted to look like St. Jerome, by the hand of Fra Bartolomeo, according to traditional accounts. Nineteenth century restoration work then cancelled this modification. In this composition the touch of Ghirlandaio, noted for his lively narrative and decorative elements, is conspicuous in the unusual majesty of the three sculptural figures which strikingly emerge from the "chiaroscuro" effect of the niches.

53

PIETRO PERUGINO
Assumption of the Virgin

This altarpiece was located on the high altar of the church in the Benedictine Monastery of Vallombrosa. Perugino painted it with a expert technique using structures and drawings already tested on other, similar great compositions, and dwelling in his usual pleasant way on the decorative details like the Archangel Michael's sophisticated armour on the extreme right.

45

Gallery of the Slaves

The present-day Gallery of the Slaves occupies the area once called the Gallery of Antique Paintings in which, starting from 1817, a great number of Thirteenth and Fourteenth century panel paintings and polyptychs, of unknown attribution and poor state of conservation, were kept. With the arrival of the David and the creation of the Michelangelo Museum the arrangement of the Gallery was radically changed; between the Nineteenth and Twentieth century the hall was dismantled, the Medieval paintings removed, the walls decorated with tapestries and the area dedicated to exhibiting plaster casts of Michelangelo's minor works.

In 1909 the Slaves were moved from Buontalenti's Grotto in the Boboli Gardens to the Accademia Gallery, and this hall gradually became a unique collection of the great sculptor's original works. Today the arrangements of the Slaves, along the sides of the Gallery, seems purposely designed to lead the visitor, in a growing crescendo of emotion, to the feet of Michelangelo's colossus.

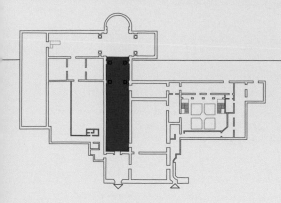

MICHELANGELO'S *SLAVES*

The four sculptures – exhibited in this room along with other works by Michelangelo and by artists influenced by him – were intended to decorate the base of a complicated mausoleum to be raised in the basilica of St. Peter's in the Vatican as the tomb of Pope Julius II della Rovere. The project had a tormented history and after undergoing radical modifications to reduce the size, the mausoleum was placed in San Pietro in Vincoli where it remains to this day. The four unfinished Slaves *not used on the tomb were donated after Michelangelo's death to Grand Duke Cosimo I de' Medici and placed by him in the Buontalenti Grotto in Boboli, from where they were transferred to the Accademia in 1909. The* Slaves *are a good introduction to an understanding of Michelangelo's unfinished work. Their forms, not brought to a state of perfection, manage to confer a universal meaning on that sensation of an immense struggle to free themselves from the marble vividly perceived by all who view them.*

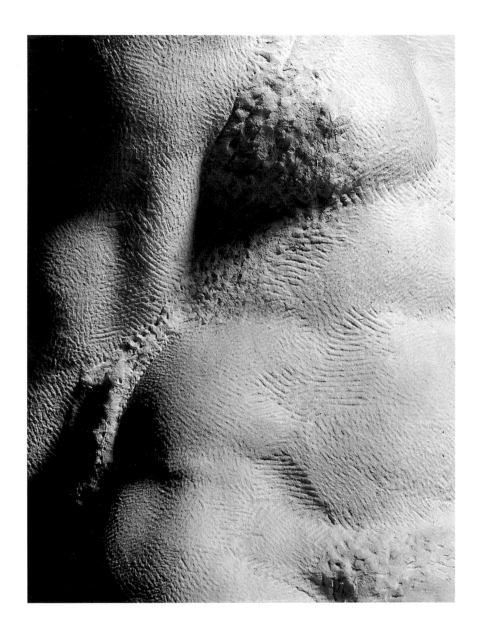

2

MICHELANGELO BUONARROTI
Slaves:
The Young Slave

The first of the four *Slaves* displayed along the walls of the Gallery leading to the Tribuna of *David* is known as *The Young Slave*. He is depicted with slightly bent knees, as if burdened by a weary step, and his left arm is folded across his face, while his right arm slips behind his hip.
Emerging from a block of marble which, at the back, seems still untouched, the different parts of the figure itself have been finished to various degrees: the head is roughly outlined, the left side of the torso more finished than the right.
However on each part of the surface the marks of the tools used by Michelangelo in his long creative process are still visible.

3

MICHELANGELO BUONARROTI
Slaves:
The Awakening Slave

The powerful limbs of this virile figure struggle to emerge from one side of the imposing block of marble.

The roughly outlined features of the face can barely be made out, and the right leg, bent over the left, protrudes forward to mirror the movement of the right arm.
The result is a tense and dynamic composition which fully expresses the struggle of the material to break out of its own limits.

6

MARIOTTO ALBERTINELLI
Annunciation

This large panel decorated the chapel of the Brotherhood of St. Zanobius at the rectory of the Cathedral of Santa Maria del Fiore in Florence. After Albertinelli's death two other painting were addet to the sides depicting the *Removal of the body of St. Zanobius* and *St. Zanobius revives a boy* by Ridolfo del Ghirlandaio, with a stylistic majesty and essentiality perhaps never previously attained in his paintings.

8

MICHELANGELO BUONARROTI
St. Matthew

The *St. Matthew* was originally to be part of a series of the twelve apostles, a commission given to
Michelangelo in 1503 for the columns of Florence
Cathedral. In the event the sculptor only worked
on one, which is also unfinished, for which reason
it was left abandoned in the Opera del Duomo
(Cathedral Vestry Board) courtyard until 1831. It
was moved to the Accademia di Belle Arti where
it was first placed in a niche in the courtyard and
later, in 1909, in the Gallery near the *Slaves*.

9

ANDREA DEL SARTO
*Christ as the Man
of Sorrows*

This fresco was removed in 1810 from the top
of the staircase leading to the novitiate in the
Santissima Annunziata Monastery in Florence.

Despite the poor condition of the work (perhaps also due to the detachment procedure
which presented greater risks in that period than
today) the figure of the suffering Christ, his
pierced hands resting wearily on the stone of
the tomb, still expresses the drama of death and
pain with great intensity.

10

MICHELANGELO BUONARROTI
Slaves:
The Bearded Slave

The Bearded Slave is the most nearly finished of the four *Slaves* by Michelangelo. The face is covered by a thick, curly beard and the thighs are encircled by a strip of cloth. The fine modelling of the torso, the surface finished with soft sensitivity to light and clear evidence of relief modelling, reveals a careful and profound study of anatomy.

The sculpture is traversed below the hips by a fracture, the origin of which is unknown.

11

MICHELANGELO BUONARROTI
Slaves: Atlas

This *Slave* is known as *Atlas* because he seems to be carrying a huge weight on his head; however the weight is in fact the head itself, which is not separate and cannot be distinguished. The legs seem to be parted and the bent arms struggle to support the massive weight bearing down on the wide shoulders. *Atlas*, perhaps more than the other *Slaves*, seems to express energy struggling to emerge from the marble.

57

12

MICHELANGELO BUONARROTI
(ATTR. TO)
Pietà from Palestrina

Among the large sculptures attributed to Michelangelo Buonarroti, the *Pietà from Palestrina* (c. 1547-1559) is the only one not recorded in the sources or in any document in the archives. It has been in the Accademia since 1939, purchased by the State of Italy from a chapel in Palazzo Barberini at Palestrina.

It was mentioned for the first time as a 'rough draft' by Michelangelo in a historical publication on Palestrina dated 1736. The lack of certain documentation led to a lengthy discussion on its attribution, involving numerous experts, after the presentation of the work in modern times (Garnier 1907).

Many art historians, noting the presence of disproportion, unusual softness of the forms and a certain flatness, have attributed this work to one of the Maestro's followers.

14

Jacopo Pontormo
Venus and Cupid

This work was painted by Jacopo Carucci, known as Pontormo, around 1533, on a preparatory cartoon drawn by Michelangelo, as can be seen from the sculptural forms of Venus and Cupid.

Presumably soon after having been painted, the nude body of Venus was covered by drapery, since this is how she appears already in the copy made by Vasari, now in Palazzo Colonna in Rome. The painting was restored to its original condition by Ulisse Forni in 1852, revealing Pontormo's nude.

17

MICHELE DI RIDOLFO DEL GHIRLANDAIO
Ideal Portrait (so-called "Zenobia")

Found in the Guardaroba Granducale along with another similar oval portrait displayed in the Galleria, this painting came from the Florentine Convento delle Stabilite, although the subject suggests that it may have been done for a private client. Standing out against a green background Zenobia, with her elaborate coiffeur, her eye seeming to follow the spectator with a courtesan's alluring gaze, shows a close resemblance to a drawing by Michelangelo dating from around 1524.

Tribuna of David

Between 1872 and 1882 the architect Emilio De Fabris designed, in the Accademia Gallery, a hall in the shape of a Latin cross at the center of which, under a circular skylight, the David *would be placed. In early August of 1873 the* David, *sliding on rails through the streets of Florence, was moved to the Accademia. Only in 1882 was work on the Tribuna and the two side wings completed.*

At first copies of Michelangelo's works were exhibited in the side wings. In the early Twentieth century the Michelangelo Museum was dismantled and the walls were decorated with tapestries. It was only in the 1980s that the tapestries were replaced by large paintings by Sixteenth century artists, to emphasize their relationship with Michelangelo's work.

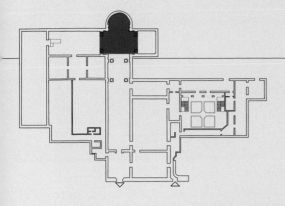

1

MICHELANGELO BUONARROTI
David

The *David* was originally commissioned by the Florence Opera del Duomo to be placed as a decoration in the Cathedral. It was sculpted by Michelangelo between 1501 and 1504, when it was placed in front of Palazzo Vecchio, following much discussion and debate among the main contemporary Florentine artists. The Giant, as it became known, became a symbol of the civil freedom and virtue of republican Florence, and it remained in its original location until 1873 when it was transferred, using a com-

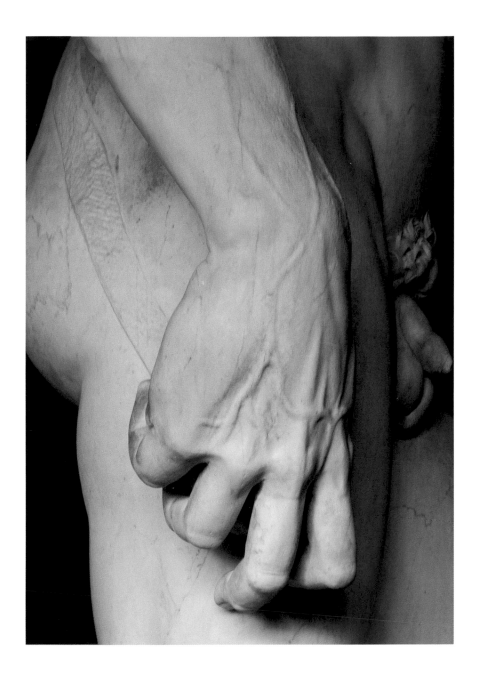

plex support structure resting on wheels, inside the Accademia di Belle Arti, where it can still be admired today.

The sculpture portrays the future king of Israel in a similar form and pose to a triumphant hero of classical Greece. This clearly distances Michelangelo's *David* from those previously made by Donatello and Verrocchio which, ad-

hering more closely to the biblical text, depicted David as a slender boy, unaware of his divine mission.

The statue's perfect modelling, the calm and determined strength of the expression and its imposing size have made it one of the best-known and most admired works of art in the world.

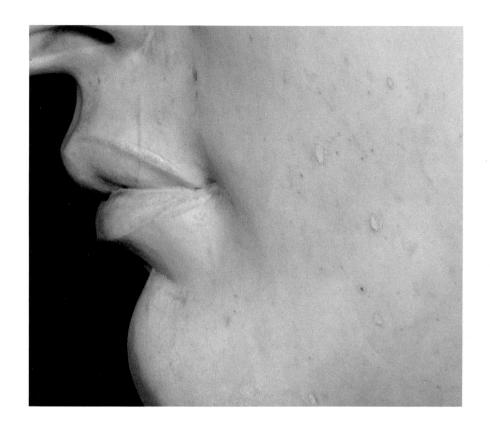

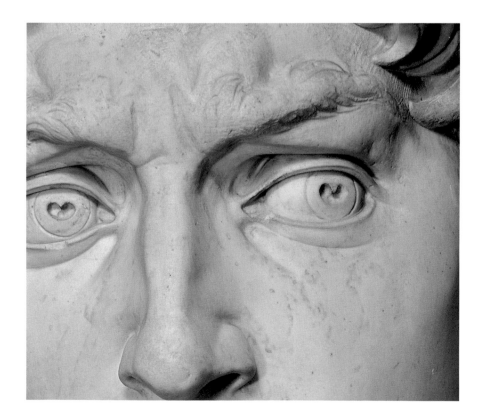

Side wings of the Tribuna

Since the beginning of the 1980s this area has housed a series of works by artists who were contemporaries of Michelangelo, or slightly later. Among these are some of Alessandro Allori's large panels.

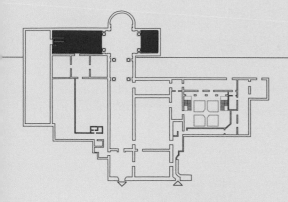

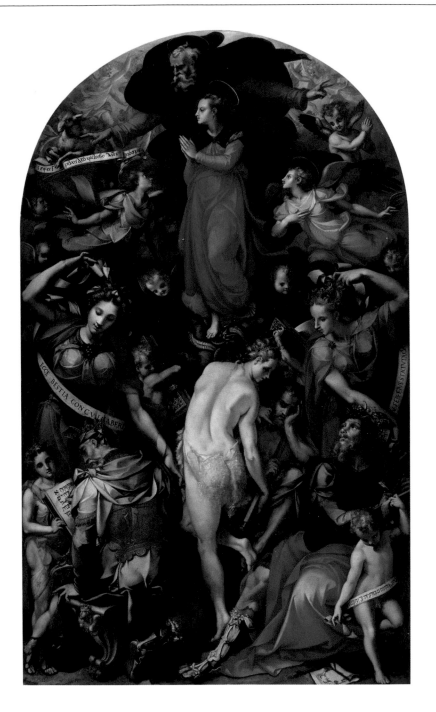

5

CARLO PORTELLI
Immaculate Conception

The painting, whose recent restoration has revived its brilliant colors and clear legibility, revealing the splendid nude Eve, was commissioned for the Church of Ognissanti in Florence. Its subject is the Immaculate Conception of Mary, a theme originating in the second half of the 15th century, but long subjected to heated debate within the Catholic Church. Portelli's strongly Mannerist style is exemplified here in the space entirely concentrated in the foreground, and in the sinuous poses of his figures, in studied contrast to one another.

SANTI DI TITO

Lamentation for Christ

This painting, which comes from the chapel in Fortezza da Basso (Florence), portrays Christ taken down from the cross, surrounded by the Virgin, Saint John the Baptist, Saint Catherine and the donor wearing ornate armor with the insignia of the Knights of Saint Stephen, recently identified, on the basis of the coat-of-arms clearly visible at his side, as Ernando Sastri of Spain. The particular sensitivity to color, clearly revealed by the restoration 2003, seems to indicate a dating around the 1590s, a period in which Titi was strongly influenced by the colorism of Cigoli.

AGNOLO BRONZINO
Deposition

This enormous painting was commissioned by Cosimo I de' Medici for the Church of the Observant Minorites at Portoferraio (Island of Elba) where it arrived transported by ship down the Arno. At the far left, above, the bearded old man in the background is a self-portrait of the artist. Although the work survived in a deplorable state of conservation, due to a devastating fire that broke out in the church, a recent difficult, lengthy restoration has revealed again its significant artistic merit.

15

ALESSANDRO ALLORI
Annunciation

This great panel, painted in 1578-1579, restored in 2003, was commissioned by Sister Laura de' Pazzi for the Convent of Montedomini, in whose church it was situated when the holy institution was suppressed and its furnishings confiscated by the State.

The severe and contained composition, suitable for a convent in a time of Counter Reformation, is softened by the charming still-life of the basket with clothes and the delicate flowers scattered on the floor.

Nineteenth Century Room

The large Nineteenth Century Room was conceived and realised in order to provide the collection of plaster casts by Lorenzo Bartolini with a stable and definitive location. However the intention was also to offer the visitor tangible evidence of the Nineteenth century academic origins of this Gallery, today mainly known for Michelangelo's David. *All around the Room run shelves on which busts of personages, most of them not identified, are displayed.*

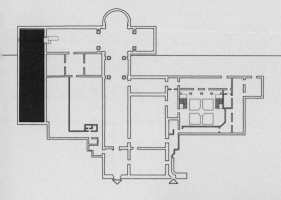

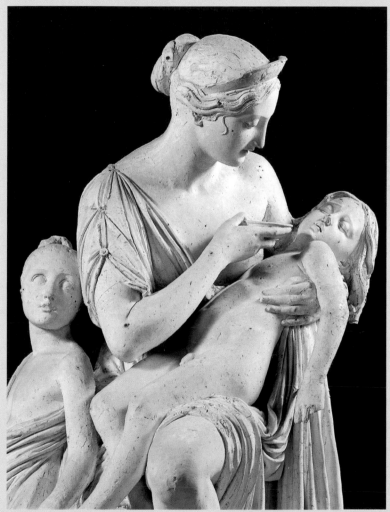

24

LORENZO BARTOLINI
Demidoff Monument

The commemorative monument to count Nikolaj Demidoff was commissioned by his sons
Paul and Anatolij in 1828, on the death of their
father. Several times interrupted and restart-
ed when the difficulties were overcome, it was
only placed where it stands today (in Piazza
Demidoff, opposite Lungarno Serristori, in Florence) in 1871. The work was finished by Ro-
manelli, a pupil of Bartolini who took over his
workshop. It was a grand and complex project,
consisting of many statues, some larger than life,
with complicated allegorical meaning. The plaster model of the central group, depicting the
count Nikolaj with his son Anatolij, has been lost.

10

LORENZO BARTOLINI
Emma and Julia Campbell

A visit to Bartolini's studio by Lady Barry, an English author who admired his work, procured the artist several commissions from the British aristocracy. Among these was the portrait of the Campbell sisters portrayed in the act of dancing commissioned by their mother Lady Charlotte Campbell, whom the artist met in Florence between September of 1819 and August of 1820. The marble original is thought to be in the dining room of the Inveraray Castle, the property of the Duke of Argyll in Scotland. Although this work is still dominated by neo-classical taste, it reveals Bartolini's early purist orientation during these years. The two girls are portrayed "in antique style", wearing sandals and classical tunics bound under the breast by narrow ribbons. On this group traces of the so-called "dots" procedure, used to mark the angles and the various depths of the points to be reproduced on the block of marble, can be detected.

73

LUIGI MUSSINI
Sacred Music

This is one of the pictures which testify to the original bond between the Accademia Gallery and the School of Accademia delle Belle Arti. Luigi Mussini painted it in Rome in 1841 as a trial for his academic pension.

In that same year it was exhibited in the Prize-winners Gallery of the Florence Accademia, where it remained for years.

The picture represents a youth with wings gazing upward toward heaven, her lips parted in a liturgical chant. *Sacred Music* is a clear and illustrious example of Purism in Tuscany, and of how Luigi Mussini shared in the experience of the Nazarenes who drew inspiration from great examples of Fifteenth and Sixteenth-centuries painting.

Luigi Mussini moreover, had the chance to learn stylistic rigor in drawing directly from the great French artist Ingres, who stayed in Florence for some time in the 1820s.

Thirteenth and Early Fourteenth C. Room

The Florentine Gothic painting route (in three rooms on the ground floor and four on the first floor) starts in this room, which house many gold-leaf background panels in an absolutely unique collection of its kind. Displayed in the central room are works by artists predating Giotto or his contemporaries, like Grifo di Tancredi and Pacino di Buonaguida; in the right-hand room are Giotto's direct followers, Taddeo Gaddi, Bernardo Daddi, Jacopo del Casentino, in addition to a fresco by Giotto himself; in the left-hand room are the Orcagnas, Giovanni da Milano and Giottino.

10

MASTER OF THE MAGDALENE
The St. Magdalene and eight Scenes from her Life

This panel, coming from the Convento della SS. Annunziata, clearly exemplifies Florentine painting before Giotto. The Master of the Magdalene set up one of the most productive studio in Florence (1265-1290), and shows evidence of attention to the innovations introduced by Cimabue. In this sense, the small side scenes, which offer a direct and lively narrative of moments from the Saint's life, are more attractive than the solemn central figure.

A conspicuous example are the naturalistic landscape elements in the background of the *Noli me tangere* (depicted in the second scene on the left).

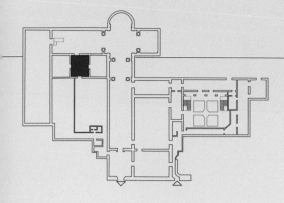

6

MASTER OF THE ST. CECILIA
Enthroned Madonna and Child

Exhibited from 1902 to 1998 in the Museo Civico of Pescia, this painting is a work fundamental for the history of Fourteenth century Florentine painting.
It is attributed to an anonymous contemporary and collaborator of Giotto, whose hand is recognisable also in some parts of the frescoes with *Scenes from the Life of St. Francis* in the upper Basilica of Assisi.

4

PACINO DI BUONAGUIDA
The Tree of Life

With its vivid colours and sophisticated drawing (Pacino was also a famous illuminator), this
painting mainly illustrates the content of St.
Bonaventure's *Lignum Vitae*, although there are
also many scenes and scrolls alluding to biblical texts.

In its entirety it appears as a large doctrinal page
for meditation as well as an image to be admired.
The subject of the illustration is the genealogy of
Christ, who is shown nailed to the tree-shaped
cross with its roots on a rocky mountain, sym-
bolising Mount Calvary.

Room of Giotto and his School

1

GIOTTO DI BONDONE AND ASSISTANTS
Head of Shepherd and herds

This fragment of a detached fresco comes from the ancient high chapel of the Church of Badia in Florence which, according to Lorenzo Ghiberti and other sources earlier than Vasari, was frescoed by Giotto, who also painted the polyptych over the high altar, now in the Uffizi Gallery. In the past this and a few other surviving pictorial fragments were not unanimously accepted by critics as authentic works by Giotto, but in recent years the pictorial quality of this shep-

herd's head – originally belonging in all probability to the scene of Joachim among the shepherds – has been noted by the greatest scholars of Giotto's art.

More than one expert has observed at most a certain stylistic diversity between the Uffizi polyptych, a key work in the development of Giotto's style around the year 1300, and this fragment, whose freshness and luminosity point to a substantially later dating, perhaps during the span of time between the painting of the frescoes in the Peruzzi chapel (c. 1310-1315) and those in the Bardi chapel (c. 1325-1330) in the Florentine Basilica of Santa Croce.

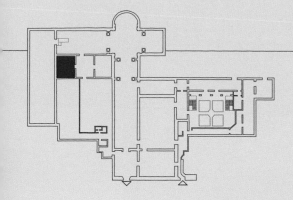

4

BERNARDO DADDI
Saint Bartholomew; *Saint Lawrence*

These two saints were part of a polyptych made for the chapel of Saint Bartholomew and Saint Lawrence in the church of the Carmine in Florence; at the polyptych's centre was a Madonna with Child and at the sides two or perhaps four Saints.

The polyptych also probably had a predella. These paintings reached us in an exceptionally integral state of preservation and allow us to fully appreciate the quality of Bernardo Daddi's work in around 1340, at the peak of his career.

9

BERNARDO DADDI
Painted Crucifix: The grieving Virgin and
St. John and *Stories of Christ's Passion*

This large, shaped *Crucifix* possibly comes from the Florentine Church of San Donato in Polverosa and was presumably placed above the high altar, hanging from the ceiling.

In medieval churches this type of image was often placed on top of the iconostasis, i.e. the dividing wall between the presbytery and the choir, as is clearly shown in the Greccio nativity scene painted by Giotto in the Basilica of St. Francis in Assisi.

11

TADDEO GADDI
Scenes from the Life of Christ;
Scenes from the Life of St. Francis of Assisi

These panels came from the sacristy of the Basilica of Santa Croce where they decorated wooden furniture, perhaps a reliquary cupboard. The single episodes from the life of St. Francis are illustrated in a parallel with the Life of Christ: for example, the episode with the *Imposition of the stigmata to St. Francis* corresponds to the *Crucifixion*. Giotto's most direct pupil, Taddeo was the first to include his master's innovations: note the solid volumetric disposition of the figures and the well-constructed architectural perspective, which indicate a *modus operandi* very far removed from the transcendent and ethereal world of Byzantine painting.

87

Room of Giovanni da Milano and the Orcagnas

2

ANDREA ORCAGNA
Pentecost

This triptych (c. 1365-1370) reveals the characteristics of Andrea Orcagna's painting style in the last phase of his life; with its square spaces, the rigid frontal arrangement of the figures and the limited chromatic range, it must have fitted harmoniously in the Romanesque Church of the Santi Apostoli in Florence, its probably place of provenance. In the second half of the Eighteenth century it was transferred to the Church of Badia, from where it was passed to the Accademia Gallery in 1939.

It is likely that Andrea's younger brother Jacopo assisted in the painting work, and his hand can be seen in areas of softer, more blended application of colour in some of the Apostles, and hints of softness in the volumetric construction.

3

NARDO DI CIONE
Thronum Gratiae; St. Romuald;
St. John the Evangelist

This polyptych was commissioned by Giovanni
Ghiberti for his chapel in the Chapter of Santa
Maria degli Angioli. It was removed and taken (c.
1750) to the Della Stufa Chapel, dedicated to St.
Andrew, and on this occasion St. John Evangelist
was repainted to resemble St. Andrew. Today the
triptych has resumed its original appearance.

6

GIOTTO DI STEFANO
KNOWN AS
GIOTTINO

Madonna and Child
Enthroned
with two Saints
and eight Angels

Originally situated behind the tabernacle at the entrance to Piazza Santo Spirito in Florence, this fresco – a supreme masterpiece of fourteenth-century Florentine painting – is one of the few works that can be attributed to Giottino, the grandson of Giotto di Bondone. Distinguished by his refined style in drawing and chiaroscuro, Giottino is recorded as having been in Rome in 1369 with Giovanni da Milano, engaged in frescoing a chapel in the Vatican Palace.

11

MASTER OF THE ACCADEMIA MISERICORDIA (GIOVANNI GADDI?)
Virgin of Mercy

This panel comes from the Augustinian Monastery of Santa Maria in Candeli. It portrays the *Virgin as Mater Misericordiae*, sheltering under her mantle, held up by two angels, twenty-three nuns and four novices, probably the donors of the tabernacle.

Once considered the work of an anonymous Fifteenth century painter, it is now attributed to a master who takes his name from this painting, to whom several other works in the same room have also been attributed.

The calligraphic elegance and delicate treatment of color seem to indicate that the painter may have worked in illumination as well. It has recently been hypothesised that the Master of the Accademia Misericordia may be Giovanni Gaddi, the elder brother of the more famous Agnolo Gaddi, documented as a painter from 1369-1386.

12

GIOVANNI DA MILANO
Christ in Pietà
lamented by the Virgin, St. Mary
Magdalene and St. John the Evangelist

This small devotional panel represents one of the greatest achievements of Fourteenth century painting in Florence after the death of Giotto. It was painted for the Florentine Church of San Girolamo alla Costa, dated 1365 and signed, and at the bottom bears the coats of arms of the Strozzi and Rinieri families who obviously commissioned it. Giovanni da Milano's painting, with its intense sensitivity to colour and moving sentimentality offers an alternative to the severe style of Orcagna, which had dominated the gloomy period following the Great Plague of 1348. With Giovanni's work, Florence opened up to the new insistence of the International Gothic trend.

15

ANDREA DI BONAIUTO
St. Agnes
St. Domitilla

Andrea di Bonaiuto (also known as Andrea da Firenze), a Florentine painter who trained in the studio of Nardo di Cione, brother of Andrea Orcagna, is famous above all for having frescoed the Spagnuoli Chapel in the Santa Maria Novella Monastery. This small diptych (c. 1365-1370) is stylistically and therefore chronologically close to that work and demonstrates the painter's knowledge and assimilation of the work of Giovanni da Milano, who was present and working in Florence in those very years. The two female figures shown here particularly stand out for the courtly sophistication of their costly clothes and the intense use of "chiaroscuro".

18

MATTEO DI PACINO
Vision of St. Bernard; Episodes from the Lives of St. Bernard, St. Benedict, St. John the Evangelist, St. Quentin and St. Galgano

The panel, attributed in the past to an anonymous Master of the Rinuccini Chapel, is now recognized as the work of Matteo di Pacino, a painter trained in the Orcagna shop and thus possessing a style marked by a strong sense of volumetric disposition and monumentality, who worked with Giovanni da Milano on the fresco decorations of the Rinuccini Chapel in Santa Croce, completing them when da Milano left Florence.

Due to his contact with Giovanni da Milano, the painter's chromatic range is warmer and brighter than that of Orcagna's closest followers.

The first two rooms on the first floor, recently restored and rearranged to offer a display as complete as possible and easy to read, contain a conspicuous number of gold-leaf panels by Florentine painters from the late of the Fourteenth Century. These include portable altarpieces and grand polyptychs, which bear witness to public and private devotion in Florence in the Gothic century.

1

WORKSHOP OF JACOPO DI CIONE
Massacre of the Innocents;
Adoration of the Magi;
Flight into Egypt

This panel was in the past attributed to an anonymous master known as the Master of Christ's Childhood because of the scenes depicted here, but has now been included in the early works of Jacopo di Cione, brother of Andrea Orcagna and quite close in his lively narrative style to Niccolò di Tommaso.

DON SILVESTRO DE' GHERARDUCCI
Madonna of Humility and Angels

Silvestro de' Gherarducci entered the Monastery of Santa Maria degli Angioli in 1348 aged nine. He worked with Lorenzo Monaco as a painter and illuminator, never losing the characteristic rich and colourful decorative elements that may have been influenced by Sienese art. The *Virgin of Humility* (c. 1370-1375), which depicts the Virgin sitting on the ground on a cushion, is a subject particularly dear to late Gothic tastes.

3

GIOVANNI DEL BIONDO
Annunciation

This large and complex polyptych, dating from around 1380-1385, was situated on the altar of the Cavalcanti Chapel in the Florentine Church of Santa Maria Novella. It came to us in excellent condition, complete with almost all its accessorie.

This polyptych constitutes an example of the high technical quality of the work of 14th century Florentine studios.

❼

SPINELLO ARETINO
St. Stephen

The saint is depicted holding in his right hand the banner of the Wool Guild, which was quite a powerful corporation in Florence and the same motif is repeated on the sides of the predella. This little tabernacle (c. 1400-1405) demonstrates the preciosity of Spinello's later style, and to a greater extent, the small *Crucifixion* in the cusp panel, where the drapery of the crouching figures flows with inimitable elegance.

8

SPINELLO ARETINO
Enthroned Madonna
with Child and four Angels;
St. Paul, St. John the Baptist,
St. Andrew and St. Matthew the Evangelist

This altarpiece, which comes from the Church of Sant'Andrea a Lucca, is signed and dated 1391 on the step in the central panel. Spinello Aretino was first trained in the vigorous artistic atmosphere of Arezzo but later worked all over Tuscany – in addition to Arezzo and Lucca, Florence, where he worked for the Opera del Duomo in 1387; Pisa, where he frescoed the *Stories of Saints Efisio and Potito* in the Camposanto; Siena, where he worked in the Cathedral in 1405 and in the Sala di Balìa in Palazzo Pubblico in 1408.

The Accademia Gallery possesses another work commissioned of Spinello, Niccolò Gerini and Lorenzo di Niccolò in 1399: the polyptych of the *Coronation of the Virgin and Saints* painted for the high altar of the Church of Santa Felicita in Florence (Inv. 1890 no. 8468). On a basic scheme that is still Giottesque, Spinello grafts episodes and details imbued with Gothic elegance in a style distinguished for its lively narration and vivid sense of decoration.

🔢13

MARIOTTO DI NARDO
Madonna and Child with Saints

This polyptych (c. 1390-1395), commissioned by the Corsini family for Church of St. Gaggio, records the mature phase of Mariotto di Nardo's work. It was an active artist in Florence between the Fourteenth and Fifteenth centuries, also for commissions of a certain importance. His success was probably due to the Orcagnesque elements in his style, the excessive hardness of which was diluted with warmer colouring and more charming decorative elements. The work by Mariotto reached us complete with all its elements, i.e. the predella showing *Scenes from the Life of the Virgin* and the large cuspidate panels with *Annunciation* and *Crucifixion*, and thus provides us with an idea of how ornate the altars of the most important Medieval churches must have been.

16

NICCOLÒ DI PIETRO GERINI
Christ as the Man of Sorrows
with the Symbols of the Passion

This panel (c. 1404-1408) is a typical example of the work of the painter Niccolò di Pietro Gerini and comes from the Disciplinary Company of the Pellegrino in Santa Maria Novella in Florence. The brethren of the Company are depicted on the cusp kneeling in the foreground before Christ pilgrim, and on the predella in the act of burying one of the members of their Company.

All the brethren wear white cloaks and their heads are covered by hoods, in order not to be recognised while carrying out works of charity. At the centre Christ rises from the tomb, showing the wounds in his hands and side, before the cross, on which are hung the symbols of Passion: nails, whips, the spear and the sponge.

18

LORENZO MONACO
*Annunciation and St. Catherine
of Alexandria, St. Anthony abbot,
St. Proculus and St. Francis of Assisi*

Painted for the church of San Procolo in Florence, this *Annunciation* represents the peak of Lorenzo Monaco's work; in the period in which Masaccio, initiator of the artistic Renaissance, was beginning to work, the Medieval world is brought to life with brilliant success in this work (c. 1410-1415).

LORENZO MONACO
Enthroned Madonna
with Child and Saints

This polyptych (1410) formerly decorated the Church of San Bartolomeo in Montoliveto near Florence and confirms Lorenzo Monaco's ability with chromatic and decorative effects, even in works of larger dimensions.

Having now fully mastered his expressive medium, the great master emphasises here the outlines of the figures with impeccable fluidi-

ty and harmony while the chromatic range seems infused with the purest light.

It must be remembered that Lorenzo Monaco was also an illuminator and his pen decorated with gold and bright colours many of the manuscripts made in the Monastery of Santa Maria degli Angioli in Florence, where he lived as a Camaldolensian monk.

23

LORENZO MONACO
*Oration
in the Garden*

This is one of the oldest panels by Lorenzo Monaco and was painted (c. 1395-1400) for the Florentine Monastery of Santa Maria degli An-gioli, where the artist lived. His deep knowledge of Giotto's painting, who must have been directly known to him, is evident from the style, learned in the Orcagna studio. However, at the same time the fluid and extended flowing of the dra-pery places his work within the modern taste for International Gothicism.

JACOPO CAMBI
*Coronation of the Virgin
with eight Angels and fourteen Saints*

This beautiful example of embroidery in *opus florentinum*, one of the most magnificent to come down to us, decorated the high altar of the Church of Santa Maria Novella in Florence. It was probably commissioned by Fra Jacopo of Andrea Aldobrandini, who was given other commissions for furnishings for the Dominican Monastery. The main scene with the *Coronation of the Virgin* is flanked by seven figures on each side, delimited to the right by the patriarch Abraham and to the left by king David. On the upper border are eleven stories from the life of Maria. In the lower center are the signature and the date: 'IACOBUS CAMBI DE FLORENTIA ME FECIT MCCCXXXVI'. Decorations of this type were highly appreciated and widely diffused in the Fourteenth century, especially in France and Spain, where another altar-facing embroidered by Geri di Lapo is still to be found in the Cathedral of Manresa in Catalonia.

As compared to the latter, Jacopo Cambi's work is more elegant in the variety and fantasy of the stitches and in the Gothic style of the drawing. For the "ornate" naturalism of the figures and for some of the facial types (St. Peter and St. Paul), the most authoritative critics have linked this work to the refined culture of the Master of Figline.

28

ROSSELLO DI JACOPO FRANCHI

Coronation of the Virgin with Angels and Saints

This grand and highly decorated polyptych (1420) is the work of Rossello di Jacopo Franchi, an artist who trained in the late Gothic period and continued to paint his sweet and rather mannered figures until the end of his life (1456), long after the advent in Florence of Masaccio and the rise of the early Renaissance.

32

GHERARDO STARNINA
Madonna with Child,
St. John the Baptist, St. Nicolas and Angels

Gherardo Starnina, a Florentine painter who also worked in Spain where he came into contact with the most advanced trends of International Gothicism, today tends to be identified by critics as the so-called Master of the Lively Child, an outstanding figure in early Fifteenth century painting in Florence. He was noted for his linear finesse and the decorative nature of his elegant forms, and is almost a profane *alter ego* of Lorenzo Monaco.

33
MASTER
OF THE STRAUS MADONNA
Annunciation

This work came from the leper Hospital of Sant'Eusebio al Prato and is attributed to a painter who was active between the end of the Fourteenth century and the beginning of the Fifteenth. His identity is not known and he is usually known as the Master of the Straus Madonna from a *Virgin with Child* in the Straus Collection. This is a painter gifted with fine sensitivity to colour and who also pays attention to the volumetric structure of bodies and the perspective depth of the space.

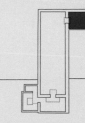

Room 3 ❖ Florence, 1370-1430 (International Gothic)

42

GIOVANNI DI FRANCESCO TOSCANI
Stigmata of St. Francis
and *Miracle of St. Nicolas of Bari*
(predella)
Crucifixion (cusp)

These two panels, dating from the beginning of the third decade of the Fifteenth century, formed part of the polyptych adorning the Ardinghelli Chapel in the Church of Santa Trinita at Florence. The painter was a Florentine artist, enrolled in the Compagnia di San Luca in 1424, known especially as a painter of chests (two of

his chests are now in the Bargello Museum). His earliest works, such the *Incredulity of St. Thomas* in the Accademia Gallery, reveal training in contact with the Orcagna circle as well as the influence of Lorenzo Ghiberti's style, particularly in the rhythmic folds of the drapery. This element has led some scholars to identify the artist as Giovanni di Francesco, one of Ghiberti's assistants for the doors of the Baptistery. Within a span of ten years Giovanni Toscani shows in these two panels how he has assimilated the innovations of the International Gothic Style introduced to Florence by Gentile da Fabriano and Arcangelo di Cola.

46

GIOVANNI DI FRANCESCO TOSCANI

*The Incredulity of Saint Thomas
The Prophets Jeremiah
and Isaiah*

Giovanni Toscani was for a long time known as the Master of the Griggs Crucifixion, before his identity was discovered in 1966. The subject matter of this panel is commented on the dado at the bottom with the words 'Touch that which is real like me and you will believe in justice combined in three people, which always exalts those who act justly'. The sentence refers to a place where justice was administered, perhaps the Court of Mercatanzia, around which he worked in 1419-1420; this date is in keeping with the Gothic characteristics of the work.

47

BICCI DI LORENZO
St. Lawrence

This panel comes from the Laical Company devoted to St. Peter at the Church of San Pietro a Monticelli. The Saint is shown standing on the symbol of his martyrdom, the grille, while in his left hand he holds the palm and in the right a red banner with a gold star, perhaps the insignia of the Corporation who commissioned the work.

In the predella, in the right-hand scene, St. Lawrence is depicted freeing souls from Purgatory, according to the legend which claims that as he died on Good Friday, he was permitted every Friday to repeat Christ's descent to the Underworld. The scene on the left shows the martyrdom inflicted on him by his persecutors. Bicci di Lorenzo painted this work in about 1428, in collaboration with Stefano d'Antonio with whom he "kept company" (or as we would say today "was in partnership") from 1426 to 1434.

115

48

MARIOTTO DI CRISTOFANO
*Scenes from the Lives
of Christ and of the Virgin*

This painting, dated from 1450-1457, coming from the Church of Sant'Andrea a Doccia (a village near Pontassieve, Florence), is made up of six panels portraying *Scenes from the Christ' childhood and from his Life*, the *Death of the Virgin*, and in the large central cusp, the *Assumption*.

The polyptych was attributed in the Nineteenth century to the school of Beato Angelico and subsequently to an artist influenced by Bicci di Lorenzo. In the 1960s it was noticed that similarities existed between this painting and the dual-face panel, present in the same room, representing the *Mystic marriage of St. Catherine of Alexandria* and the *Resurrection of Christ*, painted in 1445 by Mariotto di Cristofano, an artist whose style shows the influence of Beato Angelico and Masolino.

GIOVANNI DAL PONTE
*Coronation of the Virgin
with four musical Angels
and St. Francis, St. John the Baptist,
St. Ivo and St. Dominic*

Giovanni di Marco, known as Giovanni dal Ponte, received his nickname from the fact that he came from the florentine Parish of Santo Stefano al Ponte.

He was an artist of great skill, clearly able to assimilate into his original artistic language the cultural influences emanating from the broad panorama of Florentine art in the early Fifteenth century. The artist was first attracted by Spinello Aretino, then by the Gothic International style introduced to Florence in those years by Lorenzo Monaco and Gherardo Starnina. In the third decade of the century (c. 1420-1430), to which this polyptych is dated, he freely adopted the Renaissance innovations introduced by Masolino, Beato Angelico and Masaccio, conferring greater composure on the figures but without abandoning his propensity to impetuous rhythms in the drawing as well as in the drapery of the figures.

The Icons

After the transferral to the Galleria degli Uffizi of the substantial group of Russian icons originally moved to the Galleria in 1771 from the Guardaroba of the Grand Dukes of Lorraine, the five icons of Veneto-Byzantine art, coming mainly from the suppression of churches and monasteries in the late 18th-early 19th century, have been rearranged and displayed in Room 1 on the first floor. The best known of them is the Madonna of the Passion, *signed by the Cretan painter Andrea Ritzos, of which various versions are known.*

84

ANDREA RITZOS DA CANDIA

Madonna of the Passion (Madonna and Child, Angels and the Instruments of the Passion)

The icon is signed by the renowned painter from Crete active in the 15th century in Candia. The painting comes from the Franciscan monastery of San Girolamo at Fiesole (Florence).

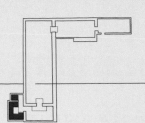

83

CRETAN-VENETIAN SCHOOL (ATTR. TO NIKOLAOS RITZOS)
*Saints Peter and Paul
presenting a Temple to God*

The two Saints hold in their right hands the model of a polygonal church surmounted by a cupola. Inside the building is the iconostasis of Orthodox churches and, at the centre an altar prepared for the celebration of the Eucharist. From the heavenly vault Christ, seen in half-figure, bestows blessings on the Apostles.

46 GIOVANNI DI FRANCESCO TOSCANI
Incredulity of St. Thomas
In the cusp:
The Prophets Jeremiah and Isaiah
c. 1420
Tempera on wood
242×123 cm
Inv. 1890 no. 457

47 BICCI DI LORENZO
St. Lawrence
In the predella: *Scenes
from the Life of St. Lawrence*
c. 1428
Tempera on wood
236×99 cm
Inv. 1890 no. 471

48 MARIOTTO DI CRISTOFANO
*Scenes from the Lives of Christ
and of the Virgin*
In the cusps: *Annunciation*
and *Assumption of the Virgin*
c. 1450-1457
Tempera on wood
263,5×184 cm
Inv. 1890 no. 8508
Restored: 2004

49. BICCI DI LORENZO
Mystic marriage of St. Catherine
c. 1423-1425
Tempera on wood
127×62 cm
Inv. 1890 no. 8611

50 GIOVANNI DAL PONTE
*Coronation of the Virgin
with four musical Angels
and St. Francis, St. John the
Baptist, St. Ivo and St. Dominic*
In the cusps: *Descent into Limbo
Annunciation*
c. 1420-1430
Tempera on wood
208×215.5 cm
Inv. 1890 no. 458ù

Collection of Icons

1. SCHOOL OF MOSCOW
Annual Menology on two panels
1. *Months from September to February*
2. *Months from March to August*
Second quarter of the 18th century
Mixed technique on wood
70×54 cm (each)
Inv. 1890 nos. 5954, 5955

2. SCHOOL OF MOSCOW
Dormitio Virginis
16th-17th century
Mixed technique on wood
31.2×25.1 cm
Inv. 1890 no. 9356

3. SCHOOL OF MOSCOW
Ascension
16th-17th century
Mixed technique on wood; 31×26.4 cm
Inv. 1890 no. 9357

4. BYZANTINE SCHOOL
Dormitio Virginis
15th century
Tempera on wood; 44.5×31 cm
Inv. 1890 no. 6147

5. RUSSIAN SCHOOL
*The Prophet Elijah in the Desert
with scenes from his Life*
First half of the 18th century
Mixed technique on wood
31.2×28.5 cm
Inv. 1890 no. 6174

6. RUSSIAN SCHOOL
Ascension
17th-18th century
Mixed technique on wood; 30.9×26.1 cm
Inv. 1890 no. 9365

7. RUSSIAN SCHOOL
Nativity of the Virgin
18th century
Mixed technique on wood
30.7×25.6 cm
Inv. 1890 no. 9368

8. RUSSIAN SCHOOL
*"In You all creatures rejoice"
(The Virgin Enthroned
and in Glory)*
Last quarter of the 16th century
Mixed technique on wood
32.2×26.2 cm
Inv. 1890 no. 9354

9. RUSSIAN SCHOOL
Beheading of John the Baptist
End of 17th century
Mixed technique on wood; 32.2×26 cm
Inv. 1890 no. 9355

10. RUSSIAN SCHOOL
The Redeemer in Glory with Saints
18th century
Mixed technique on wood
30.8×26.9 cm
Inv. 1890 no. 9369

11. RUSSIAN SCHOOL
*St. Nicholas of Myra
and six scenes from his Life*
18th century
Mixed technique on wood
32×27.5 cm
Inv. 1890 no. 9323

12. RUSSIAN SCHOOL
The fruits of Christ's Passion
Second quarter of the 18th century
Mixed technique on wood
36×29.5 cm
Inv. 1890 no. 9342

13. RUSSIAN SCHOOL
Death of the Mother of God
Second quarter of the 18th century
Mixed technique on wood
35.6×29.8 cm
Inv. 1890 no. 9300

14. RUSSIAN SCHOOL
*Nativity of Christ
and other scenes
from His infancy*
17th century
Mixed technique on wood
35.5×29.9 cm
Inv. 1890 no. 9301

15. RUSSIAN SCHOOL
Madonna of Mercy
18th century
Mixed technique on wood
24.8×21.1 cm
Inv. 1890 no. 9324

16. RUSSIAN SCHOOL
The seven Martyrs of Ephesus
18th century
Mixed technique on wood
31×27 cm
Inv. 1890 no. 9337

17. RUSSIAN SCHOOL
*The Resurrection
with other Russian "festivals"*
17th century
Mixed technique on wood
33×27.3 cm
Inv. 1890 no. 9348

18. RUSSIAN SCHOOL
*The Resurrection
with episodes and figures
from the New Testament*
18th century
Mixed technique on wood
35×30 cm
Inv. 1890 no. 9349

19. Russian School
*The Virgin in Glory
with Archangels, Prophets
and Saints*
18th century
Mixed technique on wood; 30.2×25.1 cm
Inv. 1890 no. 9363

20. Russian School
*Cavalcade of the Magi;
Adoration of the Magi;
Flight into Egypt*
Second quarter of the 18th century
Mixed technique on wood; 30.6×26 cm
Inv. 1890 no. 9364

21. Russian School
Madonna of Mercy
18th century
Mixed technique on wood
30.9×26.1 cm
Inv. 1890 no. 9367

22. Russian School
St. Nicholas
18th century
Mixed technique on wood; 25.5×21 cm
Inv. 1890 no. 9325

23. Russian School
Resurrection
18th century
Mixed technique on wood; 11×9 cm
Inv. 1890 no. 9310

24. Russian School
Pentecost
18th century
Mixed technique on wood 11.5×80.5
cm
Inv. 1890 no. 9311

25. Russian School
Nativity of the Virgin
18th century
Mixed technique on wood; 11×9 cm
Inv. 1890 no. 9312

26. Russian School
*The Assumption
and Coronation of the Virgin*
18th century
Mixed technique on wood; 10.7×9 cm
Inv. 1890 no. 9319

27. Russian School
Nativity of the Virgin
18th century
Mixed technique on wood
13×11 cm
Inv. 1890 no. 9303

28. Scuola russa
Transfiguration
18th century
Mixed technique on wood; 13×11 cm
Inv. 1890 no. 9309

29. Russian School
Transfiguration
18th century
Mixed technique on wood
12.5×10.5 cm
Inv. 1890 no. 9313

30. Russian School
Madonna della Misericordia
18th century
; 12,5×10.5 cm
Inv. 1890 no. 9316

31. Russian School
*Vision of the Sacristan Juriš
with scenes of Russian festivals*
Second quarter of the 18th century
Mixed technique on wood
35.5×29 cm
Inv. 1890 no. 9343

32. Russian School
The Redeemer enthroned
18th century
Mixed technique on wood
13×11 cm
Inv. 1890 no. 9302

33. Russian School
Adoration of the Shepherds
18th century
Mixed technique on wood
13×11 cm
Inv. 1890 no. 9305

34. Russian School
Resurrection
18th century
Mixed technique on wood
13×11 cm
Inv. 1890 no. 9306

35. Russian School
Resurrection of Lazarus
18th century
Mixed technique on wood
13×11 cm
Inv. 1890 no. 9307

36. Russian School
Crucifixion
18th century
Mixed technique on wood
13×11 cm
Inv. 1890 no. 9308

37. Russian School
Resurrection of Lazarus
18th century
Mixed technique on wood; 13×11 cm
Inv. 1890 no. 9314

38. Russian School
*St. Lazarus
of Thessalonica*
18th century
Mixed technique on wood
13×10.8 cm
Inv. 1890 no. 9321

39. Russian School
The seven Martyrs of Ephesus
18th century
Mixed technique on wood
13×10 cm
Inv. 1890 no. 9326

40. Russian School
Adoration of the Magi
18th century
Mixed technique on wood; 13×11 cm
Inv. 1890 no. 9327

41. Russian School
*St. Joachim
and St. Anne*
18th century
Mixed technique on wood
13.5×11 cm
Inv. 1890 no. 9328

42. Russian School
"Madonna del latte"
18th century
Mixed technique on wood
13×11 cm
Inv. 1890 no. 9329

43. Russian School
St. Michael
18th century
Mixed technique on wood
13.5×11 cm
Inv. 1890 no. 9330

44. Russian School
St. Demetrius
18th century
Mixed technique on wood
13×10.5 cm
Inv. 1890 no. 9332

45. Russian School
St. Spiridion Bishop of Trimithunte
Second quarter of the 18th century
Mixed technique on wood; 13×11 cm
Inv. 1890 no. 9333

46. RUSSIAN SCHOOL
Annunciation
18th century
Mixed technique on wood; 13×10 cm
Inv. 1890 no. 9334

47. RUSSIAN SCHOOL
Misericordia
(The Mother of God
"Joy of all those afflicted")
17th century
Mixed technique on wood
13×10.5 cm
Inv. 1890 no. 9335

48. RUSSIAN SCHOOL
The seven Martyrs of Ephesus
18th century
Mixed technique on wood; 13×11 cm
Inv. 1890 no. 9336

49. RUSSIAN SCHOOL
Annunciation
18th century
Mixed technique on wood; 13×11 cm
Inv. 1890 no. 9304

50. RUSSIAN SCHOOL
Christ in Glory
with seven Hierarchies of Angels
18th century
Mixed technique on wood
19.5×11 cm
Inv. 1890 no. 9315

51. RUSSIAN SCHOOL
Panels of a Deesis
18th century
Mixed technique on wood
8×19.7 cm
Inv. 1890 no. 9317

52. RUSSIAN SCHOOL
Pantocrator
18th century
Mixed technique on wood
10.5×90.7 cm
Inv. 1890 no. 9318

53. RUSSIAN SCHOOL
Virgin of Vladimir
18th century
Mixed technique on wood; 11×10 cm
Inv. 1890 no. 9320

54. RUSSIAN SCHOOL
Resurrection, Descent into Hell,
with Evangelical scenes
Second half of the 17th century
Mixed technique on wood; 31×27 cm
Inv. 1890 no. 9338

55. RUSSIAN SCHOOL
The Tree of Jesse
Second half of the 18th century
Mixed technique on wood
30.6×27.1 cm
Inv. 1890 no. 6171

56. RUSSIAN SCHOOL
St. John the Warrior
and six scenes from his life
18th century
Mixed technique on wood
35.4×29.8 cm
Inv. 1890 no. 9358

57. RUSSIAN SCHOOL
Madonna of Mercy
18th century
Mixed technique on wood
35.6×30 cm
Inv. 1890 no. 9359

58. RUSSIAN SCHOOL
Ascension
17th-18th century
Mixed technique on wood;
19.7×17.5 cm
Inv. 1890 no. 9331

59. RUSSIAN SCHOOL
St. George and the Princess
18th century
Mixed technique on wood
30.8×26.9 cm
Inv. 1890 no. 6175

60. RUSSIAN SCHOOL
St. John the Theologist
in silence
Second quarter
of the 18th century
Mixed technique on wood
31.9×27.6 cm
Inv. 1890 no. 9322

61. RUSSIAN SCHOOL
Abraham visited
by the Angels
or the Holy Trinity
Second quarter
of the 18th century
Mixed technique on wood
32.1×27.2 cm
Inv. 1890 no. 9352

62. RUSSIAN SCHOOL
Annunciation
18th century
Mixed technique on wood
32.1×27.6 cm
Inv. 1890 no. 9353

63. RUSSIAN SCHOOL
St. John the Soldier
and four scenes from his life
18th century
Mixed technique on wood
31×26 cm
Inv. 1890 no. 9361

64. RUSSIAN SCHOOL
Transfiguration
18th century
Mixed technique on wood
31×26 cm
Inv. 1890 no. 9362

65. RUSSIAN SCHOOL
St. John the Baptist
and two scenes from his life
18th century
Mixed technique on wood
31.7×27.3 cm
Inv. 1890 no. 9366

66. RUSSIAN SCHOOL
Nativity of the Virgin
and scenes from the life
of St. Joachim and St. Anne
18th century
Mixed technique on wood
30.5×26.2 cm
Inv. 1890 no. 6173

67. RUSSIAN SCHOOL
The Archangel Michael
on a fiery horse defeats
the AntiChrist
Second quarter of the 18th century
Mixed technique on wood
30.7×26.7 cm
Inv. 1890 no. 9344

68. RUSSIAN SCHOOL
Annunciation
18th century
Mixed technique on wood
30×27 cm
Inv. 1890 no. 9345

69. RUSSIAN SCHOOL
Pietà
18th century
Mixed technique on wood
31.9×27 cm
Inv. 1890 no. 9340

70. RUSSIAN SCHOOL
Salvatore Acheropita
First half of the 18th century
Mixed technique on wood
31×25.7 cm
Inv. 1890 no. 9341

71. RUSSIAN SCHOOL
Nativity of the Virgin
18th century
Mixed technique on wood
30.8×26.3 cm
Inv. 1890 no. 9350

72. RUSSIAN SCHOOL
The Virgin in Glory,
the Eternal Father and Saints
First half of the 18th century
Mixed technique on wood: 30×26 cm
Inv. 1890 no. 6172

73. RUSSIAN SCHOOL
The Mother of God
"Joy of all those afflicted
1734
Mixed technique on wood; 27×23 cm
Inv. 1890 no. 9346

74. RUSSIAN SCHOOL
The Virgin of Kazan
Second quarter of the 18th century
Mixed technique on wood
54.1×46.5 cm
Inv. 1890 no. 9339

75. RUSSIAN SCHOOL
The Resurrection
and scenes from the Passion
Second quarter of the 18th century
Mixed technique on wood
62.4×64.3 cm
Inv. 1890 no. 9360

76. RUSSIAN SCHOOL
"Acheropita" borne up by Angels
18th century
Mixed technique on wood; 30.5×27 cm
Inv. 1890 no. 9351

77. VASILIJ GRJAZNOV
Madonna of Tichvin
1728
Mixed technique on wood
31×25.5 cm
Inv. 1890 no. 9347

77. RUSSIAN SCHOOL
St. Catherine of Alexandria
Late 17th century
Mixed technique on wood; 32×27.4 cm
Inv. 1890 no. 5979

79. RUSSIAN SCHOOL
Protection of the Mother of God
First half of the 19th century
Mixed technique on wood
44.3×37.3 cm
Inv. 1890 no. 9620

80. CRETAN-VENITIAN SCHOOL
Virgin and Child,
Angels, Saints
and Prophets
15th century
Mixed technique on wood
60×57 cm
Inv. 1890 no. 431

81. ADRIATIC SCHOOL
Adoration of the Magi
16th century
Mixed technique on wood
45×39 cm
Inv. 1890 no. 7284

82. DALMATIC SCHOOL
Pietà
18th century
Mixed technique on wood
27×18.5 cm
Inv. 1890 no. 6615

83 CRETAN-VENITIAN SCHOOL
(attr. to NIKOLAOS RITZOS)
Saints Peter and Paul
presenting a Temple to God
Second half of the 15th century
Mixed technique on wood
52×41 cm
Inv. 1890 no. 9382

84. ANDREA RITZOS
DA CANDIA
Madonna of the Passion
(*Madonna and Child, Angels*
and the Instruments of the Passion)
15th century
Mixed technique on wood
70×54 cm
Inv. 1890 no. 3886

85. BYZANTINE SCHOOL
St. John the Baptist
16th century
Mixed technique on wood
50×38 cm
Inv. 1890 no. 8721

Works not
on display

BICCI DI LORENZO
St. Andrew and St. Michael
St. Jerome and St. Lawrence
c. 1435
Tempera on wood
175×58.5 cm (each)
Deposits Inv. no. 12

BICCI DI LORENZO
St. Paul; St. Benedict;
St. Giovanni Gualberto;
St. Peter
c. 1430-1435
Tempera on wood
54×19 cm (each)
Inv. 1890 nos. 5985, 5986, 5987, 5988

BICCI DI LORENZO
The Holy Apostles
c. 1420
Tempera on wood
55×19.5 cm (each)
Inv. 1890 nos. 6141, 6143, 6141;
6142, 6142, 6143

BERNARDO DADDI
Enthroned Madonna with Child
between two Angels,
St. John the Baptist
and St. Luke
1333
Tempera on wood
219×132 cm
Inv. 1890 no. 6170

BERNARDO DADDI
Enthroned Madonna
with Child
1335-1340
Tempera on wood
248×110 cm
Inv. 1890 no. 3466

FLORENTINE PAINTER
St. Peter and St. Eustace
(On the back: *The prophet*
Jeremiah and Angel's head);
St. Nicolas and St. Peter
(On the back: *The Prophet Isaiah*
[?] and Angel's head);
St. Reparata (or Dorothy)
and St. James
(On the back: *Angel with thurible*);
St. Jerome and Saint with book
(On the back: *Angel with thurible*)
c. 1410
Tempera on wood
64×26 cm (each)
Inv. 1890 nos. 6116, 6117, 6118,
6132
Restored: 1995

FLORENTINE PAINTER
Virgin of Humility
between two Angels
c. 1390-1399
Tempera on wood
102×54 cm
Inv. 1890 no. 465

AGNOLO GADDI
Madonna "del latte"
and Saints (Catherine
of Alexandria and John
the Baptist; Mary Magdalene
and Anthony abbot)
c. 1380
Tempera on wood; 140×65 cm
Inv. 1890 no. 8577

NICCOLÒ DI PIETRO GERINI
Enthroned Madonna and Child
with two Saints
c. 1400-1410
Tempera on wood; 301×128.5 cm
Inv. 1890 no. 439

NICCOLÒ DI PIETRO GERINI
Madonna with Child and Saints
Beginning 15th century
Tempera on wood; 136.5×64.5 cm
Inv. 1890 no. 8578

GIOVANNI DAL PONTE
St. Helen and *St. James Major*
1420-1430
Tempera on wood; 94×39.5 (each)
Inv. 1890 nos. 8746, 8744

GIOVANNI DAL PONTE
St. Julian; St. John the Baptist
c. 1430
Tempera on wood
59×26 cm (each)
Inv. 1890 nos. 6232, 6105

LORENZO DI BICCI
St. Julian and St. Zanobius
c. 1380-1400
Tempera on wood; 131×82.5 cm
Inv. 1890 no. 5410

LORENZO DI NICCOLÒ
Coronation of the Virgin
with four musical Angels;
St. Zanobius
and St. Bartholomew
c. 1400-1410
Tempera on wood; 156×174 cm
Inv. 1890 nos. 6087, 6088, 4656
Restored: 1995 (both compartments)

LORENZO MONACO
Christ Crucified and Angels;
Sorrowing Virgin (right);
St. John the Evangelist (left)
c. 1400-1413
Tempera on wood
78×65 cm; 74×18 cm; 78×65 cm
Inv. 1890 nos. 2141, 2169, 2140
Restored: 2004

MARIOTTO DI NARDO
Annunciation
c. 1400-1410
Tempera on wood
165.5×155 cm
Inv. 1890 no. 463

MARIOTTO DI NARDO (below)
Crucifixion and four Stories
of Life of St. Nicolas
c. 1410-1415
Tempera on wood
40×242 cm
Inv. 1890 no. 9206
Restored: 1985

MARIOTTO DI NARDO
Madonna with Child and Saints
(Philip and John the Baptist)
In the cusp: *Two Angels*
c. 1418
Tempera on wood
244×126 cm
Inv. 1890 no. 473

MASTER OF BORGO
ALLA COLLINA
(SCOLAIO DI GIOVANNI)
Crucifixion among the Virgin,
St. Francis and kneeling donor
First half of 15th century
Tempera on wood; 70×51.5 cm
Inv. 1890 no. 3149

MASTER OF BORGO
ALLA COLLINA
(SCOLAIO DI GIOVANNI)
Enthroned Madonna
with Child and Saints
c. 1430
Tempera on wood
140×67 cm
Inv. 1890 no. 3159

MASTER OF SANT'IVO
Madonna and Child
with four Saints
(Apollonia, John the Baptist,
Anthony abbot and a Saint)
c. 1390-1410
Tempera on wood
70×51.5 cm
Inv. 1890 no. 3151

MASTER OF SANT'IVO
Madonna with Child and Saints
(Anthony abbot, Francis of Assisi,
Dorothea and a Saint)
c. 1400-1415
Tempera on wood; 77×42 cm
Inv. 1890 no. 8614

MASTER OF THE ACCADEMIA
MISERICORDIA (GIOVANNI GADDI)
Madonna with Child and Saints
1370-1380
Tempera on wood; 90×48 cm;
Deposit Inv. no. 1761

MASTER OF THE ASHMOLEAN
MUSEUM PREDELLA
St. Lawrence; St. Vescovus
1360-1365
Tempera on wood
84×31.8 cm; 87×31.5 cm.
Inv. 1890 nos. 8702, 8701

MASTER OF THE STRAUS MADONNA
Triptych: Madonna and Child
between St. Matthew
and the Archangel Michael
c. 1385
Tempera on wood; 141×196 cm
Inv. 1890 no. 3072

MATTEO DI PACINO
Charity of St. Anthony abbot
1370-1375
Tempera on wood; 53.5×49.5 cm
Inv. 1890 no. 460

PUCCIO DI SIMONE
St. Matthew enthroned and Angels;
St. Deacon; St. James Major
c 1355
In the predella:
Vir dolorum, Madonna
and St. John the Evangelist sorrows
Tempera on wood;
189×99; 167×67; 166×66.5 cm
Inv. 1890 no. 5063

ROSSELLO DI JACOPO FRANCHI
St. John the Baptist; St. Francis
c. 1400-1410
Tempera on wood
135×68.5 cm (each)
Inv. 1890 nos. 6094, 6103

GIOVANNI DI FRANCESCO TOSCANI
Madonna and Child with two
musical Angels and two Saints
1423-1424
Tempera on wood; 148×102 cm
Inv. 1890 no. 5919 Restored: 1986

UNKNOWN FLORENTINE PAINTER
Coronation of the Virgin with Saints
In the cusp:
Blessing of the Eternal Father
c. 1390-1399
Tempera on wood; 111×53 cm
Inv. 1890 no. 8579

Index